the Forth Naturalist and Historian

University of Stirling

The Journal was launched in 1975 after the 1974 British Association Meeting at Stirling in order to provide a medium for papers and information relevent to naturalist and historical interests of the Forth / mid Scotland area – that is as comprised by the Stirling, Falkirk, and Clackmannanshire authorities. As such an information resource it complements and succeeds the notable *Transactions of the Stirling Field and Archaeological Society* published from 1878 to 1939.

As of this year 2002, 25 annual volumes have been published, each one has yearly Weather and Bird reports for this Forth area, and some eight and more naturalist and historical papers, some book reviews, and notes.

Four `Contents and Indexes` are available for the years 1975 to 2002 (volumes 1 to 24 each of some 130 or more pages) at £1 each plus 50p p&p. . Volumes : 1 – 5, 1975 - 1980 (1987); 6 – 10, 1981 - 1988 (1989); 11 – 15, 1989 – 1992 (1993); 16 - 24, 1993 – 2001 (2002).

Volumes : 1 – 7, 9 – 11, 13, 14, 17 are now out of print.

All other volumes up to 23 are available at £2 each (plus £1 each p&p if posted)

Vol 8 1983-4 114pp. Pond ecology – Tailend Moss; It`s your Region – naturally; Some insects of East Flanders Moss; Robert Kidston – palaeobotanist; Attitudes of Stirling clergy to pauperism, poor relief, poverty, 1790 - 1845; Oral history of the Hillfoots textile industry......

Vol 12 1990 128pp. Dutch Elm disease; Flowers of West Fife; Queen Mary at Alloa Tower; The coal and railway industries of Clackmannanshire; Stirling Libraries community heritage project...

Vol 15 1992 124pp. Global warming; Check list of the birds of central Scotland; Tropical fern ..Airthrey Loch; Rock art…introduction; Prehistoric rock art ..Menteith; St. Margaret, Queen of Scotland; Communion services in Georgian Stirlingshire; Quoiting in central Scotland; Alloa port, ships, shipbuilding...

Vol 16 1993 130pp. University Jubilee Issue. Recent changes in weather; Birds – a conservationist`s view; Bird communities in oak and Norway spruce woodlands of Loch Lomondside; Heronry at Gartcairn Wood; Lime supply 14th to 18th centuries; Sport and recreation – 25 years of change; Bridge of Allan spa; the University`s impact on Stirling; Voters of Clackmannan in 1832; Allan Mair, the last Stirling execution...

Vol 18 1995 140pp. Bathymetric resurvey of Lake Menteith; Wintering birds of farming landscapes; Forestry in the Ochils; Founding of Thornhill; J D Adam..animal painter; Clan Gregor ... Rannoch; Further Notes on Menteith 1 Cunninghame Graham country; Textiles and planned villages of Endrick; First school board of Tulliallan....

Vol 19 1996 144pp. Landscape and Geology of Clackmannanshire; the Corbetts of central Scotland; RSPB Inversnaid Nature Reserve – the first 10 years; Wildlife garden - history of the Jupiter Project; HSE – . ...
environmental database; Prehistoric art – Castleton; Stirling Presbytery, 1604 -1612...; Further Notes on ..
Menteith 2 John Graham of Duchray......

Vol 20 1997 130pp. Limestone workings in Glen Tye; the Raven; Chequered Skipper and butterfly . .. ..
conservation; First in Fish culture, Sir James Maitland and Howieton; Grangemouth since 1900; Scotland`s
Liberator -Wallace; Barbour to Braveheart...Welsh Lecture; the Old Stirling Bridge...; Stirling Blackfriars...;
Shell midden at Braehead...

Vol 21 1998 144pp. Global warming; Bo`mains meadow; David Douglas; Lawhill wood; Wallace Oak; ....
James Watt surveys; Harvey`s `Lost child`; Robert Kirk; the Kinrosses; Built and archaeological heritage....

Vol 22 1999 156pp. CARSE; Wallacebank nature reserve; Dragonflies; Falkirk flora; Brambles of Trossachs .
. and Stirling; Man and the Landscape symposia; AHMS; Wallace Oak - supplement, and Torwood; George
Harvey; Sheriffmuir Atlantic wall; My Stirling – remembered; Bridges of the Forth....

Vol 23 2000 148pp. Flanders Moss 1998 MIRES conference papers - Geomorphology; Vegetation; . . .
Conservation and trees; Paleoenvironment and archaeology; Wintering and breeding birds of set-aside; ..
Native woodlands project; Biodiversity – Falkirk; the Falkirk Wheel; Cowane Hospital garden; St Mary`s
Aberfoyle; Music in Stirling; Early football – Callander; Bannockburn revealed......

Volumes 24 2001, and 25 2002 - are available at full price £6 each - plus p&p £1 each if posted

Vol 24 2001 140pp. ISBN 1 898008 42 6. Pollen analyses - historic landscape - Ashentrool, Menstrie Glen;
30 years of weather; Spiders of Flanders Moss; Dragonflies ...of Forth; Bill Brackenridge; 40 years of
SFAS; Cunningham of Alva; the Stirlings of Keir; Glasgow`s water; the Trossachs in art......

Vol 25 2002 112pp. ISBN 1 898008 47 7. Weather of 2002; Forth area bird report; Scotland`s rarest . . ..
butterflies; Harvie-Brown – ornithologist; Freshwater fish of LL&T National Park; Brackenridge memorial
project; Thistle and the Rose, Treaty of Perpetual Peace 1502 –the Stirling conference; The political context;
and synopses of other papers; Writers and artists of LL&T National Park; Stirling Unionist Club 1901-19;
... Rev. Duncan MacFarlan......

Some journal papers are available in pamphlet form and are listed and priced under `Publications`; others maybe
made available on request.

Offers of papers, reviews, notes, relevant to our subjects and area are welcome. All papers are refereed. Send
contributions to the Editor -Dr Neville Dix University of Stirling FK9 4LA or 7 Laurelhill Place Stirling FK8 2JH

Inquiries / orders to - Hon. Secy. Forth Naturalist and Historian Lindsay Corbett University of Stirling FK9 4LA
or 30 Dunmar Drive Alloa FK10 2EH e mail lindsay.corbett@stir.ac.uk fax 01786 494994

A charitable body (SCO 13270) founded in 1975 to promote central Scotland's environment and heritage. Member of the Scottish Publishers Association.

The Forth Naturalist and Historian (FNH) is a Stirling University (SU) informal enterprise. The Board was set up in 1975 by several Stirling University and Central Regional Council staff to provide a focus for interests, activities, meetings and publications of naturalist, environmental, heritage and historical studies for the mid Scotland area.

The annual FNH journal volumes act as an authoritative successor to that basic resource *Transactions of the Stirling Field and Archaeological Society* 1878-1939. The Journal and other FNH and associated publications are major information sources for mid Scotland.

Orders/enquiries to Honorary Editor/Secy L Corbett, University of Stirling FK9 4LA or 30 Dunmar Drive, Alloa FK10 2EH tel: (01259) 215091; Fax (01786) 464994; Telex 777557 SunivG; E-mail lindsay.corbett@stir.ac.uk; Web-http://www.stir.ac.uk/departments/naturalsciences/Forth. Titles here are FNH, plus shared, commissioned, and promoted publications. FNH titles are on Web by Book Data Ltd - www.thebookplace.com. also Amazon, BLPC, BOL.

A   **THE FORTH NATURALIST & HISTORIAN** - annual - from 1976 is supported by BP. Each volume of c130pp. has climate and bird reports for the mid Scotland area, 6 to 8 other naturalist and historical articles, book reviews and notes. Back vols are available at reduced prices (p&p £1,) - Vols 3, 4, 7, 8, 10, 12 at £1.00; 1, 5, 11,13, 16 at £2; 15 £3; 2, 6, 9 and 14 are op. Four 5yr List/Indexes 1-, 6-, 11- 80p. 16-20 £1.50. Some papers are available as separates additional to those in section C, e.g. Ashfield Factory Village; Climate, Bird and Flora papers; c 5p per page.

Papers/notes for publication are welcomed, also offers of presentations to the annual (Nov) symposium 'Man and the Landscape'.

Vol 17 1994, £4 (1.898008.02.7) incl. Mineral specimens recovery - Silver Mine; Community woodlands; Mountain Hare in the Ochils; Clackmannan Rivers Survey; New light on RLS; Stirling Ancient Bridge; Sir D Bruce; Blairlogie; A rare grass and a rare dragonfly.

Vol 18 1995, £3 (1.898008.07.1) 140pp incl. Bathymetric Survey of Menteith; Wintering Birds; Ochils Forestry; Thornhill; Adam - animal painter; Clan Gregor; Cunninghame-Graham Country; Endrick Valley Textiles; Tulliallan Schoolboard.

Vol 19 £3 (1.898008.12.4) 144pp incl. Landscape of Clackmannanshire; Corbetts (hills); Inversnaid; Jupiter; HSE-CD Rom; Prehistoric Art Castleton; Stirling presbytory; Graham of Duchray; Man and the Landscape Symposium.

Vol 20 (1.898005.17.5) £6 Limestone and Flora, Glen Tye; The Raven; Chequered Skipper and Butterfly Conservation; Sir John Maitland; Grangemouth since 1600; Stirling Bridge; Blackfriars; Shell Midden Alloa.

Vol 21 £6 1998-144 pp. (1.898008.32.9). Global warming: Bo'mains meadow; David Douglas; Lawhill woodland; Wallace Oak; James Watt surveys; Harvey's 'Lost' child; Robert Kirk. The Kinrosses; Raploch; Archaeology/Heritage of Forth; a Stirling church.

Vol 22 £6 1999 (1.898008.32.9) includes - Brambles; Falkirk flora; Dragonflies; Wallacebank Wood; Wallace Oak supplement; Sheriffmuir archaeology; Stirling 70 years ago; Sir G Harvey; Man and the Landscape Symposium; Heritage Association; CARSE; Bridges of the Forth.

Vol 23 £6 2000 (1.898 008.37.X) four papers on Flanders Moss - geomorphology, vegetation, conservation, trees. Birds of set-aside; Ochils woodlands; Biodiversity; Falkirk Wheel; Cowane's garden; Music in Stirling; Early football at Callander; St Marys Church, Aberfoyle.

Vol 24 £6 2001 (1-898808.42.6) 30 years weather; Spiders of Flanders Moss; Cunningham of Alva; Stirlings sof Keir; Glasgow's Water Supply; The Trossachs in Art; Dragonflies; Hermitage Wood.

B   **BOOKS**

AIRTHREY AND BRIDGE OF ALLAN- guided walk incl. Hermitage Wood. rev. ed. 40pp, (0-9514147.9.8). £1.85 (p&p70) reduced £1

ALL FOR A HANDFUL OF SEED. David Douglas, A K Smith £7.99 (p&p £1)

ALLOA TOWER and THE ERSKINES of MAR new edition CFSS/FAT. 30pp (1973, 78, 86) - distribution FNH £2 (p&p 70)

CALATRIA. Journal of the Falkirk Local History Society. Half-yearly from Nov.1991- vol 11 is Nov 97 £3.50 (p&p80).

CENTRAL SCOTLAND - Land, Wildlife, People. 230pp. £5 (p&p £2.00) $10.95. (1.898008.00.0) (a bargain book initially £12.50).

DOUNE - postcards from the past, McKenzie. 40pp. 1988. £2.50 (p&p60) (0.9506962.9.3) (reprinted 2001)

ENCHANTMENT OF THE TROSSACHS - Fairy traditions. Louis Stott. 32pp. £2.40 (p&p 70).

FALKIRK LIFE and TIMES. I Scott. 190 pp. J. Donald. £9 (p&p £1.20).

FALKIRK OR PARADISE - The Battle 1746, G. Bailey, 250pp. J. Donald £9 (p&p£1.20)

HISTORICAL LANDSCAPE OF LOCH LOMOND & TROSSACHS - 32pp. RCAHMS. £5 (p&p £1)

THE ISLANDS OF LOCH LOMOND - FOOTPRINTS FROM THE PAST. 36pp FOLL £5 (p&p £1).

HISTORY OF DUNBLANE - BURGH SURVEYS services. SCP. £12 (p&p £1.50)

THE LURE OF LOCH LOMOND - islands and environs. 60pp £3.95 (p&p70) $7.95 US. $8.95 AUS/NZ. (0.9514147.6.3) reduced to £2+p&p.

THE MAKING OF MODERN STIRLING. J. Lannon: 130pp. 1983 (0.950692.4.2) reprint '96 £4 (p&p80)

MINES AND MINERALS OF THE OCHILS. CFSS/FNH. 44pp. 1994, reprint. £2 (p&p80).

NEWSLETTERS OF CFSS (two per year) Current issue £1, others 40p as available (p&p 70). 5 yr contents/indexes 60p each.

THE OCHIL HILLS - Landscape, Wildlife, Heritage, Walks. 60pp. May '94. (CFSS/FNH (0.9506962.3.4) £3.50 (p&p 80) reduced to £2.50.

THE OCHILS: Place names, history, traditions. Watson. Perth Lib. 160pp. £10.95 (p&p 1.50).

RING OF WORDS - Literary Landmarks L. Stott (1) Stirling Clacks £2.95; (2) Argyll £2.95; (3) Loch Lomond £3.95 (p&p 80).

STIRLING REGION. D. Timms. Survey by SU for BA meeting 1974 £2 (p&p£2) nat. hist. chapters succeeded by Central Scotland above

STIRLING JOURNAL INDEX, Vol. 3 1920-1970. £2 + p&p £2.50 if not collectable. Vols. 1+2 1827- are op.

STIRLING'S ROAD TO MASS CULTURE: a history of social change. T. Lannon 1978 and 1993. 30pp. 60p (p&p 60).

A WEEK AT BRIDGE OF ALLAN - historic tour of Forth area. Roger. Reprint 1853 400pp S Lib. £6 (p&p110)

WELL SHELTERED & WATERED. MENSTRIE GLEN - 72pp. RCAHMS. £5 (p&p £1)

WOOLLEN MILLS OF THE HILLFOOTS - B Park. 180pp 1996 reprint £5 (p&p£1.50) (0.9506962.1.8) Reduced £4+p&p.

C   PAMPHLETS - these are reprints of papers in the annual FNH. Other papers may be available as separates all ab + 5 pp page.

AIRTHREY ROADS. Captain Haldane's magic roundabout Mackay/Angus £1.50.

ALLAN MAIR - last person executed in Stirling. C. Mair. 80p.

ALLOA AND THE HILLFOOTS TEXTILE INDUSTRY - Scobie 60p

ALLOA PORT, SHIPS AND SHIPBUILDING. J. Archibald 60p.

THE ANCIENT BRIDGE OF STIRLING - new survey. Page. 60p

BETWEEN CARRON and AVON - the Grangemouth area since 1600. Harrison £1.50

BRIDGE OF ALLAN - heritage of music and Museum Hall. G. Millar. £1.

BRIDGE OF ALLAN - Queen of Scottish Spas - 19C development. A. Durie. 80p.

CLAN GREGOR and RANNOCH. S. McGregor - £1

DICKENS at BRIDGE OF ALLAN and STIRLING JAIL - Royal hunt of a lion. D. Angus 60p.

EARLY GRAVESTONES IN HOLY RUDE CHURCHYARD. J. Harrison. £1.50.

LAUNCHING FORTH - the neglected River, Alloa to Stirling - D Angus 60p

ORAL HISTORY OF THE HILLFOOTS TEXTILE INDUSTRY. Scobie 80p

PLANTS.OF.FALKIRK DISTRICT. N. Stewart £1.50

QUEEN MARY at ALLOA TOWER, 1566. D. Angus. £1

SMITH, T S - artist, founder of Stirling's Art Gallery and Museum. Jamieson and Paton. £1.00

ST MARGARET, QUEEN OF SCOTLAND. S Macpherson. 60p

STEVENSON AT BRIDGE OF ALLAN. D Angus. £1

STEVENSON and the TROSSACHS. L. Stott. 80p

SCOTTISH ENCLOSURES - 18C FARMING AND LANDSCAPE. L Stewart £1

STRANDING OF A BOTTLE -NOSED WHALE. Maclaren. 60p

THORNHILL, founding 1696. Dixon. 80p

D   MAPS

GODFREY 15"/m prints of 25"/m 1890s OS maps, folded (some available flat) 25 titles of local places in association with FNH - Alloa; Alva/Tullibody/Menstrie; Balfron/Killearn; Bannockburn; Bathgate; Bo'ness; Bridge of Allan; Doune/Callander; Clackmannan and Kincardine; Denny; Dollar/Muckhart; Dunblane East & West; Dunipace; Falkirk; Grangemouth; Larbert/Stenhousemuir; Linlithgow; Polmont; Stirling - 4 maps - St Ninians; Stirling North; Stirling 1896; Stirling and District; Tillicoultry. Also available - Perth, Dundee, Kilmarnock, Edinburgh, Aberdeen and Glasgow areas; and others in Scotland. NB All with historical notes or in adjoining maps e.g. for Denny see Dunipace; Dunblane West see Dunblane East; for the four Stirling maps see Stirling 1896 and Stirling and District. Several are scarce or op eg. Stirling North; Stirling and District, Grangemouth. At reduced price £2 (p&p60). (from RRP £2.10)

Titles out of print:- Clackmannanshire guide to historical sources; Muckhart; History of old Stirling; This is my town (Falkirk); Firth of Forth Wildlife; Doune and Kilmadock; also FNH annual volumes 2, 6, 9 and 14.

Discount terms to trade, and to societies, plus cost of delivery for small orders. Pay on order or within 30 days, or sale/return (90 at less discount), to Forth Naturalist and Historian - cheques or by BACS Bank of Scotland 12.20.26. Acc 01941883 non-sterling acceptable.

NB. Godfrey's Old OS Maps, full series (over 1000 at £2.10) - available on web (alangodfreymaps.co.uk).

(LC April 02)

Please supply to: Name...

Address..

....Tele...

Post code..   Order ref:..

Number of copies ...., Title..price................p&p.............

Number of copies............, Title..price................p&p.............

Number of copies............, Title..price................p&p.............

Total £ ....   Cheque enclosed payable to 'Forth Naturalist and Historian')/or please invoice

To: L Corbett, Hon Sec, Forth Naturalist/Historian, University of Stirling, FK9 4LA, or 30 Dunmar Drive, Alloa, FK10 2EH.

the Forth
Naturalist
*and*Historian

Volume 25

Forth Naturalist and Historian, volume 25

Published by the Forth Naturalist and Historian, University of Stirling – an approved charity and member of the Scottish Publishers Association. 2002.

ISSN 0309-7560

ISBN 1-898008-47-7

Supported by BP in Scotland.

Cover: front– The Treaty of Perpetual Peace, 1502 – the English version, with
              James IV and Margaret Tudor. By courtesy of Historic Scotland
              and The National Archives of Scotland. (Similarly sourced, the
              Scottish version of the Treaty is in the Macdougall paper.)
        back– Inversnaid – linking Loch Lomond and the Trossachs. By
              courtesy of Mike Trubridge. (Relevant to the paper by Louis
              Stott.)

Printed by Meigle Colour Printers Ltd., Tweedbank Industrial Estate, Galashiels.
Set in Zapf Calligraphic on Edixion 100 gsm and cover Go Gloss Art 250 gsm.

THE WEATHER OF 2001

S.J. Harrison

Introduction

The historical record will, no doubt, show that the average air temperature in 2001 was again above the long-term average, continuing the apparent warming trend of recent decades. However, closer examination quickly shows that the temperature was below average for more than half of the year and only substantially above average in the very warm months of May and October. In the latter, the mean temperature was more than 3°C above average. The most remarkable features of 2001 were the sequence of monthly rainfalls that were well below average, and the lowest annual rainfall, at 70 % of the long-term average since records began at the University in 1971. By the end of June the six-months rainfall amounted to only 60 % of the long-term average, but despite this there were no serious water shortages over the summer. Only in July and October did rainfall exceed the average for the month. The year was remarkable also for a general lack of extreme weather, the only spell of exceptionally severe weather being the February snow storms.

Air temperature and rainfall figures in the following refer to Parkhead station unless indicated otherwise

January Cool and relatively dry. Cold mid-month

Snow was lying on the first day of 2001 but mild air and heavy rain resulted in a rapid thaw. While the light winds remained in the south, temperatures remained above freezing, but the weather was unsettled with occasional wet spells. Night-time temperatures began to fall and by the morning of the 9th the air temperature had fallen to –0.2°C (–0.9°C Bridge of Allan). The weather was very settled until the 17th and under clear night skies the air temperature fell well below freezing. A minimum temperature of –7.5°C was reached early on the 17th but had already fallen to –8.7°C in Bridge of Allan on the 15th. Freezing fog persisted all day on the 16th and the maximum temperature reached only –2.2°C in Bridge of Allan. On the 17th, cloud moved in from the west bringing a change to dull weather, and by the 18th there were occasional snow flurries in the cold Arctic air. The cold spell persisted until late on the 21st. From the 22nd, rainfall was intermittent and at times heavy but there were a number of lengthy sunny spells. Temperatures again fell below freezing under relatively clear night skies from the 28th. Cloud and rain returned late on the 29th and the weather had become dull and damp by the end of the month.

February Wintry with heavy snow and frost, but occasionally mild

The first three days were dull with rain and sleet. Scotland's weather was dominated by cold continental air and snow began to fall late on the 3rd. Snow fell over much of the northern half of Scotland on the 4th and 5th, which were cold and very raw days. Blizzard conditions in parts of Scotland caused widespread disruption. The snow began to ease on the 6th and a rapid thaw began in a freshening south-westerly breeze. This resulted in local flooding and the Allan was over its banks in the early hours of the 7th. There was a brief respite from the wet weather on the 8th and 9th but night temperatures fell below freezing, the grass minimum temperature falling to –9.0°C early on the 9th. Unsettled weather returned for two days, heralded by very heavy rain late on the 9th, and the Allan was again over its banks on the 11th. Between the 14th and the 20th, there were many bright sunny days with mostly light winds and early morning hoar frost. Dense fog formed during the morning of the 17th and persisted all day. By the 23rd the wind had veered to the north and there were snow flurries by the 24th. More substantial snow began to fall on the 26th which was accompanied by a freshening north-easterly wind. Many parts of Scotland experienced blizzard conditions and there was widespread disruption to road and rail travel due to drifting snow.

March Cold and very wintry at times

Snow still lay on the ground at the start of the month and lingered until the 5th. The weather was very cold with moderate to severe night frosts and occasional snow flurries. The minimum temperature had fallen to –7.5°C (–11.4°C Bridge of Allan) by dawn on the 1st. Temperatures increased on the 6th in a mild southerly breeze. The weather then became unsettled with occasional rain until the 14th. There was very heavy overnight rain between the 11th and 12th (15.0 mm). The wind then moved round towards a cold northerly direction and by the 15th snow, in the form of showers, had returned. More substantial snow fell on the 18th when it was lying at 09.00 h. Cloud increased from the south-west and by the 22nd the weather had become dull with occasional rain, although amounts were very small. A raw easterly wind persisted until late on the 27th. Wet and very windy conditions, and much warmer air, arrived late on the 30th and by the 31st the daytime temperature had risen to a more seasonal 13.2°C (13.4°C Bridge of Allan).

April Cold at times but some spring sunshine

Mild weather continued for the first two days but as the wind veered westerly on the 3rd, showers began to fall as sleet and hail. Frost was widespread on the 4th. Rain fell in a freshening westerly breeze late on the 5th and through the 6th. The weather remained unsettled until the 10th but there were some lengthy spells of warm and sunny weather over the following five days. By the 15th polar air began to affect the British Isles and the Easter weekend was bright and clear. Showers began to fall on the 17th, which had turned to snow and ice pellets by the 18th. The night temperature fell below freezing (–0.5°C) on the 20th, marking the last of the spring frosts. The 22nd and 23rd were dull and very wet days (13.2 mm) which characterised the weather for the remainder of the month.

May Dry and very warm

The first twelve days were warm and dry and by the 12th the daytime temperature had reached 24.3°C (26.6°C Bridge of Allan) which was the warmest day of the year at Parkhead. Early morning cloud tended to clear and most days were warm and very sunny. Under clear skies the night-time temperature fell quite sharply but no frosts were recorded. The warm weather brought out an exceptional show of tree blossom and lasted until late on the15th when rain began to fall. Settled weather returned on the 18th bringing a gradual return to hot and dry weather after a cloudy start. The 21st to 27th were hot and mainly dry, the daytime temperature reaching 28.9°C in Bridge of Allan on the 23rd. A fresh westerly breeze developed on the 27th and the remainder of the month was cloudy at times with occasional light rain or showers. This was the summer of 2001 !!

June Cool with some dry spells

The showery westerly wind persisted for two days but the wind veered to the north and it felt cold in the fresh breeze on the 2nd. The weather was very settled between the 3rd and the 13th providing some lengthy dry and sunny spells, but there was occasional rain that was very heavy at times and accompanied by thunder on the 7th. Torrential rain fell on afternoon of the 9th, amounting to 11.6 mm in Bridge of Allan. From the 14th the weather became dull and damp but rainfall amounts were negligible. A fresh to strong, and quite cold, north-easterly breeze developed on the 15th and 16th. Rain returned late on the 18th, which persisted all day on the 19th (14.0 mm). After a brief spell of more settled, but rather humid, weather between the 21st and 25th, conditions had become thundery by the 26th, which was a very hot day in many areas. Thunderstorms affected much of Scotland on the 26th but conditions remained warm and very humid on the 27th. There was a change to cooler fresher weather by 29th but this was accompanied by further thundery outbreaks.

July Warm at the beginning and end, but cold and wet mid-month

The first two days were hot and humid but rainless, but the following six days were very warm with lengthy and localised spells of exceptionally heavy rain, notably on the 2nd and 7th. 24.7 mm was registered in Bridge of Allan on the 7th. After a brief dry spell on the 9th, the wind became fresh to strong south-westerly and there were lengthy spells of rain, which amounted to 16.5 mm on the 10th. Unsettled weather with occasional rain lingered until the 15th when the days became sunny and quite warm for a while. Unsettled weather arrived from the west between the 20th and 24th, although rainfall amounts were slight and there were some lengthy sunny spells. It then remained dull and rather cloudy until the 28th when a freshening westerly breeze developed, which was accompanied by heavy rain late on the 30th.

August Very warm at times but damp until mid-month

The first two days were dull and wet, but the clouds cleared away on the 3rd. The 4th to the 6th very quite dry and warm, the temperature reaching 21.5°C on the 6th (24.0°C. Bridge of Allan). Rain fell on the 7th and 8th, which were followed by two relatively dry sunny days on the 9th and 10th before unsettled and wet weather returned on the 11th. The 16th to 18th were sunny and quite warm before heavy and continuous rain fell on the 19th, the wettest day of the month (14.5 mm Bridge of Allan). A spell of calmer and warmer weather began on the 21st, which lasted until the end of the month. There was occasional rain and dull conditions, notably between the 29th and 30th, but on the whole days were warm and sunny, reaching a relatively modest, but nevertheless welcome, 22.0°C on the 31st.

September Moderately warm, especially at night, and relatively dry until the last week

There was a small amount of rain on the 1st and 2nd but the weather became settled and a long spell of relatively dry weather with long sunny periods lasted until the 12th. The daytime temperature reached 20.0°C on the 5th. There was a brief wet interlude on the 12th and 13th followed by showers in a cool north-westerly breeze. There was a further spell of calm dry weather between the 17th and 23rd, and the grass minimum temperature in Bridge of Allan fell to –0.5°C early on the 18th. There were three very dull days from the 21st and the days between the 24th and 28th were very changeable with rain but lengthy sunny spells. By late on the 31st, torrential rain was falling in a very strong south westerly wind. By the next morning, 22.0 mm of rain had fallen (27.9 mm Bridge of Allan).

October Exceptionally mild and very wet

A strong, and very wet, south westerly airflow affected Scotland over the first three days. The 27.2 mm of rain that fell on the 1st brought the 48-hour total fall to 49.2 mm. The weather remained unsettled and wet until the 8th. Rain was registered every day and the wind was variable, becoming strong southerly late on the 7th. There were two fresh, but relatively dry, days on the 8th and 9th before rain returned on the 10th. A rain bearing weather system became slow-moving over southern Scotland on the 12th, which produced very heavy rain on the 14th as it began to ease northwards (14.5 mm). Days were very dull and damp with low cloud, showers and longer spells of rain but a particular feature was the daytime temperature, which exceeded 16°C on the 15th, 17th and 18th. Heavy continuous rain began to fall on the afternoon of the 21st and cloud and rain dominated the following days until the 31st. By the end of the month, the average temperature for October was the highest on record over most of the British Isles.

November Frequently mild, and generally drier than usual

The first three days were dry and sunny in a fresh westerly breeze. The air temperature fell during the evenings in the clear polar air and had fallen below freezing by the early hours of the 5th. However, wet weather moved rapidly into Scotland from the west on the 5th and by 09.00 the weather had become dull and damp with drizzle, which turned to heavy rain later. Heavy rain returned again on the 7th (11.5 mm) and as the wind veered towards the north, this began to fall as snow, and a light dusting was lying on the local hills down to 150 m on the 8th. Further snow showers fell on the 8th and, while the wind remained in the north, the weather remained cold. Warmer air moved northwards into Scotland in the early hours of the 10th which provided two mild days with sunny spells. The daytime temperature reached 15.2°C on the 10th. Cold polar air returned to Scotland on the 12th bringing a return to cold conditions, and on the 13th the daytime temperature reached only 5.7°C (5.1°C Bridge of Allan). Settled conditions arrived on the 14th which gave four calm days with occasional fog that persisted through the day on the 14th. Rain returned on the 18th and the weather became rather unsettled for the remainder of the month. On the 27th cold polar air brought a brief spell of cold weather with sleet and snow and a daytime maximum temperature of 5.5°C on the 27th. Milder and very wet weather returned late on the 28th and the 29th was a dull and very wet day (12.5 mm).

December   Very cold and exceptionally dry

The weather remained very changeable over the first six days. The 5th and 6th were dull and damp days with rain and low cloud, but this was the last spell of wet weather until after Christmas. Settled weather became firmly established over the east of the British Isles by the 7th bringing a spell of dry weather, and with the wind in the south the daytime temperatures exceeded 12°C. The minimum temperature had fallen only to 7.5°C by the morning of the 8th. The days between the 9th and 13th were calm and clear with almost cloudless skies and heavy hoar frosts. The minimum temperature early on the 10th reached –6.5°C. The temperature in Bridge of Allan stayed below 3°C between the 10th and 12th. Cloud moved in from the south-east late on the 13th and the 14th to the 16th were dull and damp with frequent drizzle. Night frosts returned on the 17th. Scotland was brought into a cold polar airflow on the 19th and snow began to fall on higher ground. By the 21st, light snow was falling in the Stirling area promising a white Christmas. Rain and milder conditions moved into Scotland from the north-west on the 23rd. Cold polar air returned late on the 24th and snow and sleet fell on higher ground. On the 27th the rain gradually began to fall as sleet, then snow, in a fresh to strong north-westerly wind. The rain and sleet died away late on the 28th leaving Scotland in bright polar air and the final days of 2001 were bright and sunny, but with moderate night frosts.

Noteworthy weather events during 2001

The following notes have been compiled from personal diaries, various press reports, the Royal Meteorological Society's 'Weather Log', and the monthly bulletins of the Climatological Observers' Link

Snowstorms blocked roads and railways, and brought down power-lines twice during February and, when the snow melted it caused flooding.

Snowstorms February 4-6th: A deep depression crossed southern England between the 4th and 6th, resulting in a strong easterly airflow across Scotland, which arrived from a cold continent. Snow began to fall overnight between the 3rd and 4th and by the morning there a was widespread cover of snow across Scotland which drifted in a strong easterly wind. Fife recorded its worst snow since 1980 and there were drifts 7 metres deep on the A93 at Glenshee. Snowdrifts 6 metres deep were common across Scotland. Most minor roads and a number of major roads were declared impassable, all schools in Shetland and a large number in Grampian were closed, and, paradoxically ski resorts were closed because of high winds and drifting snow. On the 6th a train travelling north from Inverness to Wick and Thurso became stuck in a snowdrift near Kinbrace and the passengers had to be rescued by a local farmer. By the 7th food supplies were beginning to run out in the outer isles but as the wind shifted to the south-west a thaw set in, which resulted in flooding in many parts of Scotland.

Snowstorms February 25-27th: As a deepening depression moved quickly eastwards across the British Isles it pulled in cold Arctic air in its wake. Snow had started falling by the 24th but by the afternoon of the 26th this was falling in a very strong and gusty north-easterly wind. By the 27th large parts of Scotland had been brought to a standstill by blizzards. Lanarkshire reported 31 hours of continuous snowfall accumulating to 50 cm on level ground and drifting to more than 3 metres. Sporting fixtures had to be cancelled and all roads in some regions were either closed or passable only with care. Over 100 000 homes in Scotland were without electricity and all schools in Edinburgh were reported to be closed, Both the East Coast and West Coast Main Lines were closed. The M8 was blocked for more than ten hours and more than 300 people spent several hours stuck in snow on the M74 in Lanarkshire. Fife was considered to be virtually cut off from the outside world for a while. Arctic air persisted into March, with further snowfall, but most snow thawed rapidly as temperatures increased on the 5th in a south-westerly airflow.

Bridge of Allan Flood Diary 2001

During 2001, the Allan overtopped its banks in Bridge of Allan on the following dates: February 7th, February 11th.

Postscript

The end of 2001 marks the end of most of the climate services which the University has been able to offer over the last twenty years, and the last of the weather reports for the Forth Naturalist and Historian. It is uncertain what level of service, if any, will be offered in future. Weather readings have already been discontinued at the Bridge of Allan and Flanders Moss climate stations, and the latter has been dismantled – unfortunately just before the storms of January 28th. The Parkhead station will continue to operate and comment on observations may be obtainable from Stuart Bradley in Environmental Science or Lewis Taylor in Biological Sciences at the University of Stirling.

Editor's Note

John has left the university to follow a new career. We thank him for producing this information on a regular basis over the last 27 years.

BOOK REVIEW

Rain. Brian Cathcart. Granta Publications. 100pp. London. ISBN 1 86207 534 4. £5.99

Getting used to a new kind of rain, and more of it, now in year 2000 on, this booklet comes in the context of archives of unique accurate weather records in Britain going back into the mid-eighteenth century. The change is furious – not now the traditional British drizzle, but the day long deluge. The author here explores some of the human consequences of the abstraction called climate change. A book most timely discovered within weeks of the FNH's 28th annual symposium 'Scotland's Weather and Climate: Living with Change'.

BOOK REVIEWS

Cairngorms National Park: consultation on draft designation order [legislation]. May 2002. Scottish Executive, DALCAL ('Do a little change a lot'). 188pp.

This is now a highly controversial affair !! with 'wattered down' powers and boundaries in contrast with Scotland's just established first national park – Loch Lomond and the Trossachs, and the long established Lake District.

Stirling Council Area Biodiversity Plan: sunmmary of Species and Habitat action plans: volume 1. Editor Jonathan Willet. 36pp.

Well presented and illustrated – introduction and sustainable development; then the various habitats – arable, rivers, bogs, rock, upland…, and species – salmon, water vole, butterflies, moths, eagle, swift, grouse, caipercaillie …; with notes of descriptions, factors of importance, plan objectives etc …

Falkirk area Biodiversity Plan. Editor Anna Perks. Falkirk Biodiversity Partnership. 32 page print with attached disk.

The print gives an introduction to the process – and illustrated summary notes on numerous individual local habitats and species action plans; new sets of plans are to be issued each year till 2005. Habitats include – arable, estuary, rivers, woodlands, mudflats, … Species include – salmon, bats, kestral, swift, water vole, owl, … The full document is attached in disk form.

Clackmannanshire Biodiversity Action Plan: consultation draft. Editor Lynn Campbell. The Partnership. c150 pp spiral bd. unnumbered.

Introduction, think globally, act locally, and detailed notes – description, objectives, projects, personel etc – for habitats – farmland, upland, urban, water, woodland …; and for species – red squirrel, bullfinch, goldfinch, lapwing, ring ouzel, passerines, salmon, trout, argus butterflies, sticky catchfly …; glossary, consultees list.

A power of work!

FORTH AREA BIRD REPORT 2001

C.J. Henty

Seventy nine contributors appear this year, some sending individual notes either direct to the Editor or via the RSPB local group, others have assisted in the wildfowl counts. The extensive use of record cards has greatly helped the compilation of notes by species, please send in these cards arranged in the species order as in this report or in standard field guides and lists. Red Kites and Ospreys continue to do fairly well, Buzzards have become more widespread in Falkirk whilst Goldeneye nested successfully on Loch Tay. A visit to new gravel workings led to the discovery a new and large colony of Sandmartins. Amongst winter visitors the drake Smew at L.Dochart also appeared on Loch Tay and there were surprisingly large numbers of Goldeneye on the lower Devon and the Forth below Stirling, on the estuary a large flock of Great Crested Grebes made a welcome return to Kinneil. There are some interesting reports of ringed Mute and Whooper Swans. Several Spotted Redshanks, Greenshanks and Green Sandpipers wintered and the last species could well be discovered on more rivers inland. No large autumn influx of the scarcer waders occurred although there was a remarkable flock of Black Terns in early October. A strong passage of Scandinavian thrushes started with flocks of Redwings of 1000 or more in late October, but these were eclipsed by even bigger numbers of Fieldfares in early November. Many observers were delighted by big groups of Waxwings from January to March.

Most months in 2001 were cooler and dryer than average apart from May which was much warmer, July, which was wetter, and October was both. A rapid thaw of snow on Ne'er Day was the start of an unsettled spell until a week of high pressure, with frost and some freezing fog, in mid January; conditions continued cold, but cloudy with snow showers, then gave way to alternating heavy rain and sunny spells through the last week. February started with three days of rain and sleet, becoming almost blizzards until a rapid thaw on the 6th caused flooding which persisted with a week of unsettled weather. The third week of the month was frosty and sunny but led to a northerly airstream with snow, heavy on the 26th. Snow lay through most of the first week of March due to hard frosts; the second week was unsettled but then there was more snow until a wet and cold last week which became warmer only at the end of the month. Most of the first half of April was unsettled with spells of sun, a polar airstream then initially gave bright and clear weather turning to snow showers before a dull and wet end. May was mainly warm and dry except for heavy rain in mid-month (the 16th and 21st to 27th produced the warmest days of the year). Although June started dry and sunny the second half had much rain and was often cool, though there was some thunder in the last week. Through much of July it was warm with heavy showers, but it became dull with rain in the last three days. Warm but changeable conditions, occasionally very wet, dominated August, whilst early

September was mainly dry and sunny though there was some rain in the last week, heavy on the 30th. There was much rain throughout October, although it was often warm, and high pressure appeared only on the 31st. The anticyclone persisted through November, but Scotland was on its northern edge so that a series of fronts often gave light rain, and even snow showers on the 8th and 27th. After dull and damp days in early December an anticyclone became established and gave very cold, dry weather until frontal conditions produced alternating mild and snow periods from the 19th onward; at the very end of the year it was frosty and bright.

This report is compiled from a larger archive of records submitted to the local recorder under the national scheme organised by the Scottish Ornithologists Club; annual Bird Reports depend entirely on contributions from the local birdwatching community, as far as possible these are acknowledged with initials as well as the full name list in the introduction. The most important weakness in the report this year is in the sparse information available about common breeding species; this is due to Breeding Birds Survey being cancelled because of access restrictions resulting from the outbreak of foot and mouth desease. For less common species I can sometimes mention data in terms of the numbers of pairs or apparently occupied territories for particular locations. The organisers for both the estuary and the inland waters parts of the national wildfowl counts (WEBS) have made available the results for this report. These often contribute to the species accounts and there is also a separate summary for inland waters which concentrates on localities.

Several observers send in a list largely or entirely for their home locality, much of this information is not appropriate for these annual reports but it is valuable to have on record and I am keeping them in a special file. At the moment there are fifteen such lists referring to the whole district from Falkirk to Killin.

For many species the records sent in are very unrepresentative of their general distribution, this applies particularly to very common species or to those that are secretive or breed in inaccessable places. Readers can consult the the Check List published in the Forth Naturalist and Historian Vol 15, but in addition I have in this report put, after the species name, a coded summary of general distribution - which often apparently contradicts the detailed records that are published for the year.

B - Breeding status, widespread (in more than five 10 km squares)
b   "   "   , local, scarce (in fewer than five 10 km squares)
W - Winter status, widespread or often in groups of more than ten.
w -   "   "   , local, scarce (local and usually fewer than ten in a group)
P - Passage (used when species is usually absent in winter, P or p used for widespread or local as in winter status)
S or s - a few species are present in summer but do not normally breed.

Thus BW would be appropriate for Robin, B for Swallow, p for Ruff and SW for Cormorant. No status letter is used if a species occurs less than every other year.

An asterix (*) in front of the species name means that all records received have been quoted.

The SOC has pressed for a more systematic vetting of records of species that are unusual locally, this area now has an informal panel of five - C.Henty (Recorder), A. Smith, D. Orr-Ewing, A.Blair and D.Thorogood. The judging of national UK or Scottish rarities continues as before, but we have produced for the upper Forth a list of species that are scarce locally and where the records need to be supported by either a full description or sufficient evidence to remove any reasonable doubt. Any species which is a vagrant to the area, and most of those which are asterisked in this report, will come into this category. Observers should be aware that aberrant individuals of common species of birds appear quite regularly and these sometimes resemble rarities. There is also the problem of escaped cage birds and of hybridisation, a particular problem in captive wildfowl which may then appear in natural situations.

The following abbreviations have been used : AoT - apparently occupied territory, BoA - Bridge of Allan, c/n - clutch of n eggs, BBS - Breeding Bird Survey, CBC- Common Bird Census, CP - Country Park, F - Female, G – Glen, GP - gravel pit, J - juvenile, L. - Loch, NR - Nature Reserve, M - Male, ON - on nest, Res - Reservoir, SP - summer plumage, WEBS – Wetland Bird Survey, Y - young.

The area covered by the report comprises the council areas of Falkirk and Clackmannan together with Stirling, excluding Loch Lomondside and other parts of the Clyde drainage basin. Please note that we do not include the Endrick water, *i.e.* Fintry and Balfron. Records from Carron Valley Reservoir are published here but it is proposed that Clyde should cover all the forest south of the reservoir.

This report has been compiled from records submitted by:

A. Ayre, M. Anderson, A. Bell, M.V. Bell, N. Bielby, Birdline Scotland, A. Blair, M. Blunt, R.A. Broad, G.J. Brock, D.M. Bryant, D.J. Cameron, P. Carter, R. Chapman, D.&A. Christie, L. Corbett, R.&A. Daly, P. Dearing, A. Downie, A. Duncombe, A. Eckershall, D. Egerton, J. Gordon, A.C. Hannah, I. Henderson, C.J. Henty, D. Jones, R. Jones, D.S. Kerr, J.T. Knowler, M. Kobs, G.&E. Leisk, C.J. Mallett, K. MacGregor, A.K. McNeil, D.&M. Mason, A.B. Mitchell, J. Mitchell, J. Nimmo, D. Orr-Ewing, R. Osborn, G. Owens, D. Pickett, R.K. Pollock, D. Rees, H. Robb, M. Robinson, P.W. Sandeman, J. Sankie, S. Sankey, G. Scott, A. Smith, P. Stirling-Aird, D. Thorogood, A. Thiel, A. Wallace, J. Wheeler, M. White, J. N. Willett, K. Wilkinson.

Thanks are due to Prof. S.J. Harrison for a copy of the Annual Climatological Bulletin (2001), to J. Mitchell for a copy of the L.Lomond report, to P. Stirling-Aird for data from the Raptor Study Group, and to Prof. D.M. Bryant for the results of the estuary WEBS data. D. Thorogood proofread the species accounts, any remaining or subsequent errors are due to the editor.

WEBS contributors to these data, additional to report list were: B. Barker, A. Boast, R. Bullman, A. Downie, S. Easthaugh, M. Ferguson, M. Hardy, M. Kobs,

A. Moody, S. Paterson, D. Rees, P. Series, D. Shenton, J. Watson, H. Weir, M. White, T. Young.

WILDFOWL REPORT 2001-2002

This report concerns the inland waters part of this area's Wetland Bird Survey (WEBS) organised by NB and is a condensed version of a fuller report by him.

WEBS is a monthly waterfowl census under the auspices of the British Trust for Ornithology (BTO) and the Wildfowl & Wetlands Trust (WWT), it runs from September to March inclusive. For this report 'wildfowl' includes divers, grebes, cormorants, herons, swans, geese (excluding Pink-footed and Greylag for which the WWT organises separate counts), ducks and rails

This report covers the area occupied by the new local government councils of Stirling, Falkirk and Clackmannanshire (the 'region'). In total, 124 still water sites, 89 km of river and 16 km of canal were counted by 49 counters.

The following table consists of matched monthly data for total wildfowl on 25 major sites (20 still waters). Those sites holding fed Mallard have been excluded.

Month	1998/9	1999/0	2000/1	2001/2
September	2592	2939	2110	2180
October	2766	4426	3016	2934
November	3625	4465	4565	4129
December	4469	4824	4831	3758
January	4377	4367	4419	3418
February	3289	4155	3761	4274
March	2302	2259	2478	2512
Total	23420	27435	25180	23205

This season's numbers are 8 % down on the average largely due to the low figures for January and February – less than November this year, most unusual.

Still Water Sites

Standing water in Central Region amounts to 7693 hectares or 2.9 % of the area.

Turning to individual sites, the top ten along with monthly averages are listed below:- (previous season's figures in brackets)

	Site	Average	
1. (2)	Gart complex	557	(469)
2. (4)	Lake of Menteith	403	(363)
3. (1)	Gartmorn Dam	331	(534)
4. (3)	Loch Earn	316	(416)
5. (6)	Airthrey Loch	247	(269)
6. (10)	Kersiepow South Pond	198	(162)
7. (7)	Loch Venachar	168	(253)
8. (9)	L.Dochart-Iubhair	168	(220)
9. (5)	Vale of Coustry	159	(291)
10. (18)	Blairdrummond Park	146	(233)

The above table excludes sites where Mallard are reared and released for shooting. Most sites showed small changes in total numbers this season except for marked falls for Vale of Coustry & Gartmorn (latter now only 1/3 of score four years ago).

Linear Water Features: Rivers & Canals

This season coverage of the rivers length decreased somewhat, the most important gap being the stretch of the Teith between Doune and the Forth confluence. The most favoured river was the Teith with 37 birds per km, followed by the Forth – in February there were 1020 birds on the stretch above the Teith confluence. Canals scored at 4.6 per km.

SYSTEMATIC LIST

Codes – S, F and C indicate records from Stirling, Falkirk and Clackmannanshire "Districts".

*RED-THROATED DIVER *Gavia stellata* (b,w)
F   Kinneil: 3 on 28 Jan, 1 on 30 Mar & 4 May; 1 on 11 Nov & 2 Dec (DT GO). 1 Skinflats 7 Jan & 16 Dec (MVB). 1 Bo'ness 10 Feb (DMB).
S   Trossachs: noted at 1 site, Pr on 9 May (DJC). 1 L.Tay (Killin) 26 Apr (PWS). 1 Carron Valley Res 6 Oct & 3 Nov (DAC).

*BLACK-THROATED DIVER *Gavia arctica* (b,w)
F   1 Blackness 11 Nov & 30 Dec (MA).
S   Trossachs: noted at 1 site to 6 Aug, two failed nests. Probably same birds at 2nd site 26 Jul (DJC). 2 L.Tay (Killin) 26 Apr (PWS).

LITTLE GREBE *Tachybaptus ruficollis* (B,w)
     WEBS max: 53 inland in Jan, 64 in Nov (NB).
F   At Skinflats 7 Jan to 15 Feb, 29 Oct to 20 Dec, max 12 on 8 Jan & 10 on 4 Nov & 16 Dec (MA GO AB et al).
S   Breeding season: Pr+2Y Cambusmore 6 Aug (PWS); 2Pr (1 with 2Y) Airthrey 8 Jun (AT). 13 L.Lubnaig 13 Jan & 12 on 13 Nov. 9 L.Voil/Doine 13 Jan (largely frozen) & 11 on 7 Oct (NB).

GREAT CRESTED GREBE *Podiceps cristatus* (b,W)
     WEBS totals: 124 Forth estuary in Feb & 58 in Dec (DMB); 17 inland in Oct (only 1 in Jan) (NB).
F   Large flocks return to Kinneil: 105 on 28 Jan, 120 on 10 Feb, 1 on15 Apr & 17 Jun; 4 on 24 Jul, 27 on 31 Aug, 35 on 9 Sep, max 55 on 2 Dec (DT DMB et al). Also in Jan: 20 Skinflats, 26 Carriden & 60 Blackness on 7th (MVB DMB MA).
C   Gartmorn: 8 on 30 Jan, 6 on 13 Mar; 13 on 20 Nov, 1 on 18 Dec (AT).
S   In breeding season pairs noted at Lake of Menteith (2), L.Rusky, Carron Valley Res (2), Blairdrummond (2), Coustry . Single on L.Venachar 20 May.(DT DOE NB DAC). 2 prs Cambusmore from 16 Mar, both nested but in June 3 or 4 chicks seemed to be with only one of the pairs (PWS JNW).

*FULMAR *Fulmarus glacialis* (p)
F   1 ->W Blackness 11 Nov (MA). Singles at Kinneil in Sep on 1st, 9th & 22nd (DT).

GANNET *Sula bassana* (p)
F   In September (all Juvs): 16 Kinneil on 15th, 3 on 16th & 1 on 24th. 19 Skinflats on 15th & 1 on 26th. On the estuary directions were variable and many settled, however 4 flew W over Camelon on the 25th (DT GO MA).

CORMORANT *Phalacrocorax carbo* (S,W)
     WEBS max: 97 Forth Estuary in Feb & 181 in Dec (DMB). 50 inland in Jan & 80 in Dec (NB).

F   102 Grangemouth (W) 25 Feb & 101 on 16 Sep (MVB). 50 -> W at Blackness
         30 Dec (MA).
C   75 S.Alloa roost 28 Aug & 81 on 29 Dec (MVB CJH).
S   13 on Forth, Stirling-Gargunnock, in Jan (MB RC). 13 Carron Valley Res 6 Oct
         (DAC). 17 Lake of Menteith 1 Nov (NB).

GREY HERON *Ardea cinerea* (B,W)
         WEBS max: 29 Forth Estuary in Jan & 31 in Sep (DMB). 84 inland in Jan, 91 in
         Dec (NB).
F   13 Skinflats (max) 5 Jul, 10 on 25 Sep to Dec (GO MA MVB). 10 Kinneil 22 Sep
         (DT).
C   14 on Devon, Dollar-Tillicoultry, 18 Sep (DE).
S   Many records of 6 to 10 on inland waters and river stretches (WEBS).

MUTE SWAN *Cygnus olor* (B,W)
         WEBS max: 13 Forth Estuary in Feb (DMB). 156 inland in Jan, 180 in Oct (NB).
         Ringed as cygnets: Montrose 23/8/97 – at Alva 11/11/01, dead under wires.
         Glenrothes 2/8/99 – seen at Castle Park Lochan 15/11/01, via Cramond on 2/3/00
         & Hogganfield Loch 27/8/00 (per NB). Imm ringed Milngavie 13/1/01 seen
         Gartmorn 10/2/01.
         12 pairs in early autumn had 40 Juv (in addition to Falkirk records).
F   7 Prs around Falkirk, 3 failed, 4 reared 15 Juv from 20 cygnets (MA). Max at
         Skinflats 13 on 8 Feb, 14 on 13 Apr; few late in year (GO AB). 16 on Union
         Canal, Bonnybridge-Lock 16, 10 Feb (AA).
C   34 Gartmorn 10 Feb (AT). 28 on Devon below Tullibody 6 Nov (KW).
S   Max Lake of Menteith 29 on 14 Dec (NB). Pr at L.Lubnaig had 5Y on 4 Jul, 3 Juv
         11 Sep – lst success in 10 years (PWS NB).

WHOOPER SWAN *Cygnus cygnus* (W)
         WEBS inland max: 149 in Jan, 114 in Nov. % Juveniles: Jan/Feb 9% (n=122); Oct-
         Dec 22% (n = 148) (NB) – These figures can be greatly affected by the fact that
         it is often easier to count small groups and these tend to have family parties.
         Ringed adults from Iceland, seen at L.Dochart: 26 Nov, ringed 1/8/93, via
         L.Neagh in 96,97,99; 19 Dec, ringed as adult 10/8/94, via Glenshee etc in 95-99 &
         L.Dochart 12/99 (per NB).
F   Scarce – 3 Skinflats 20 Oct (1st of autumn), 7 Bonnybridge 15 Dec (DAC MA).
C   In partly harvested cereal Cambus 20 Jan to 8 Feb, max 117 on 25 Jan (NB CJH).
         39 by Devon at Gogar 27 Jan, 42 on 6 Nov & 37 on 1 Dec; 35 at Alva 3 Nov
         (probably same group, Ed) (CJH KW MVB GEL). 3 Tillicoultry 18 Sep were very
         early (DE).
S   13 L.Dochart 8 Apr - last of spring; 14 on 10 Nov (DMB PWS). By R.Forth W of
         Fallin, 93 on 14 Jan & 67 on 17 Feb (DJ) – probably interchanged with Cambus
         herd. Only large spring herd was on Thornhill Carse 17 Jan to 16 Mar, max 25
         (DR DP DT AS). 1st of autumn were in October: 10 ->SW Ashfield on 7th, 39 -
         >SW Dunblane on 10th, then 25 on Drip Carse on 19th (DP MVB NB). Later in
         autumn only one large herd, on Thornhill Carse from 11 Nov, max 38 on 30 Dec
         (DJC DR). 16 Fallin 2/9 Dec (DT).

PINK-FOOTED GOOSE *Anser brachyrhynchus* (W)
         Large flocks reported throughout the lowland areas, in the absence of regular
         coordinated counts these are difficult to interpret. A count over most of the
         Carse of Stirling gave 5400 on 11 Feb, this presumably accounted for single site
         counts of 2800 Drip Carse on 2 Jan, 1500 on Thornhill Carse on 1 Feb & 2000
         Thornhill on 17 Mar (MVB DP DT). Few in the east until April with 375 Airth on
         8th, 650 Alloa Inch on 15th & 940 on 28th (DT DMB). Spring movement to north
         was in April & included 800+220 Bridge of Allan on 24th, also 300

Blairdrummond & 44 Dunblane on the 27th (CJH DOE MVB).
The main arrival started with 44 over Skinflats 14 Sep, then 20 Kinbuck on 20th, 47 Upper Glendevon Res on 22nd, 200 Buchlyvie on 26th & 75+155 over Braes of Doune on 27th (AS GO DT AT DAC AS). In October there were in the east 700 Airth on 16th & high numbers around Skinflats with 3800 on 21st & 5000 on 27th. On the Carse of Stirling numbers rapidly built to 3710 Drip Carse on 10 Oct & 2500 Thornhill Carse 5 Nov (AB DMB CJH NB DJC). Max inland in Falkirk was 359 Slamannan on 2 Dec (NB).

*BEAN GOOSE *Anser fabalis* (W)
F   180 Slamannan 18 Nov (AB).

*WHITE-FRONTED GOOSE *Anser albifrons* (w)
S   3 (Greenland race) Lecropt 11 Feb (DT).

GREYLAG GOOSE *Anser anser* (b,W)
Substantial flocks were noted mainly on Drip/Blairdrummond/Thornhill/Lecropt carse with 845 on 2 Jan, 800 & 500 in Feb (MVB RC SE DT). Few further north except 118 Gart 17 Feb, last were 200 G.Dochart 14 Mar (NB PWS). The only "spring" numbers east of Stirling were mainly in January: 118 Blackness on 1st & 175 L.Ellrig on 14th, 400 Cambus on 18th (& 200 on 8 Feb) (MA JN CJH). The first of autumn were rather late, 162 Drip Carse 19 Oct increasing to 247 on 6 Dec. 260 roosted at N.Third Res 10 Nov & north of the carse were 271 at Gart on 6 Dec (NB BO). In the east, noted on lower Devon from 240 on 3 Nov to 429 on 2 Dec (GEL AT).

CANADA GOOSE *Branta canadensis* (b,W)
WEBS max: 103 inland in Jan, 271 in Oct (NB).
F   7 St Helen's Loch 2 Dec (NB).
S   Seven sites had record WEBS counts. Max early in year was 68 Gart 31 Jan (NB). Autumn max were 99 G.Finglas 21 Jul, 135 L.Coulter 16 Sep, 130 Lecropt 29 Sep & 100 Gart 4 Nov (MR DAC DT). Spring pairs at Lake of Menteith, L.Voil, G.Finglas Res (2,6+5Y), Cambusmore, Cowieshall Pond (DT DJC DP).

BARNACLE GOOSE *Branta leucopsis* (w)
Autumn passage larger than usual.
F   44 Skinflats 30 Sep, then all records in October: Skinflats: 175 on 4th, 210 on 7th left NW, 153 on 9th, 116 on 21st, last 8 on 14 Nov. 14 Kinneil on 6 Oct, left S on 7th (MA DMB DT MVB DJC GO). 1 Kinneil 9 May (DT).
C   7 Alloa Inches 15 Apr (DMB).
S   3 Lecropt 11 Feb, 1 Drip Carse 18 Mar. 1 Kinbuck 2 Apr (DT MVB DOE). A bird resembling a 'blue' Snow Goose at Gargunnock on 11 Feb considered a hybrid of Barnacle with "something" (DT).

*BRENT GOOSE *Branta bernicla*
F   1 pale bellied at Kincardine Bridge 21 Oct; 4 (race uncertain) Blackness 27 Oct (MVB DAC).

SHELDUCK *Tadorna tadorna* (b,W)
WEBS max: 590 Forth Estuary in Jan & 1919 in Sep (DMB).
F   Moult flock at Kinneil totalled 2920 on 24 Aug; 419 on 16 Jun. Skinflats: 222 on 7 Jan, 742 on 16 Sep & 371 on 21 Oct. 85 Skinflats Pools on 25 Mar & 26 on 22 Jun (DMB MVB AB JNW). Inland, 1 juv Lathallan pond 16 Sep & 7 Oct (JW)
C   111 Tullibody Inch 30 Jun (DMB).
S   Max 9 on Forth above Fallin 17 Feb (DJ).

WIGEON *Anas penelope* (b,W)
WEBS max: 1207 Forth Estuary in Jan & 1095 in Oct (DMB), 706 inland in Feb & 765 in Nov (NB).
F   152 Blackness 1 Dec. Kinneil: max 320 on 18 Feb, 74 on 7 Apr & 3 pr on 29th; 200

on 22 Sep, 450 on 23 Oct, 350 on 2 Dec (AS DT GO). Skinflats: Pr on 4 Jun, max 58 on 22 Dec (GO AB). 40 L.Ellrig 16 Dec (JN).

C   530 Alloa Inches 7 Jan (MVB). 50 on Devon, Alva, 3 Nov (GEL). M Cambus 30 Jun (DAC).

S   Gart Lochs (Cambusmore): 181 on 20 Feb; 281 on 6 Dec. 113 L.Dochart 11 Jan. 208 L.Venachar 18 Jan (NB). 268 Lecropt 20 Jan & 95 on 16 Dec (MVB DT). First of autumn were 6 Blairdrummond 8 Sep (DOE). Max on the upper Forth between the Teith and Gargunnock 264 in Feb & 246 in Nov (+ 62 at Frew) (RC DR). Pr Cambusmore on 8 May & 4 on7 Jun (PWS).

*GADWALL *Anas strepera*
F   M Kinneil 22 Sep (DT). M Callendar Park 24 Sep (DMM).
C   5 (3M) Cambus Pools 13 Apr & M on 24th. M Gartmorn 28 Feb & 3 (1M) on 21 Oct (AT).
S   M Gart 6 Dec (NB).

TEAL *Anas crecca* (B,W)
        WEBS max: 1838 Forth Estuary in Jan & 1377 in Dec (DMB). 1026 inland in Jan, 920 in Nov (NB).
F   Kinneil: 1004 on 7 Jan, 750 on 10 Feb, 15 on 29 Apr; 25 on 16 Aug rising to 130 22 Sep. 218 Carronmouth 11 Feb & 229 on 16 Dec. 39 Skinflats Ponds 9 Apr, 1 on 19 Jun; 46 on 27 Aug. Inland max 64 Carronshore 14 Jan & 54 on 16 Dec (DMB DT MVB GO AB).
C   On Devon: 152 Alva-Dollar in Feb & 128 in Dec. 160 Kersiepow 25 Jan & 85 on 11 Nov (GEL DE NB). 20 Cambus Pools 29 Sep. 78 Kennetpans 11 Feb & 77 on 21 Oct (CJH).
S   187 Killin marshes 7 Oct & 349 Gart on 16th. 122 L.Mahaick 9 Nov. (NB). 2 L.Dochart 19 Jun (PWS). F+2Y Flanders Moss 3 Jul & F+5Y on 19th, 80 on 25 Nov (SS DP).

MALLARD *Anas platyrhynchos* (B,W)
        WEBS max: 400 Forth Estuary in Jan & 445 in Oct (DMB), 2596 inland in Jan & 2284 in Nov (NB). 22 Broods had 148 Y, av brood size 6.7 (AT GO NB).
F   99 Skinflats 16 Dec (MVB). 190 Kinneil 31 Aug (DT). 49 Carronshore 14 Jan & 40 on 16 Dec (AB).
C   305 Gartmorn 14 Jan (AT).
S   230 N.Third Res 20 Jan (BO). 136 Cocksburn Res 4 Feb (AT). 217 Airthrey 12 Feb & 260 on 7 Oct (MK). 186 Killin Marshes 7 Oct. 238 Blairdrummond Safari Park Pond 24 Oct (NB).

PINTAIL *Anas acuta* (W)
F   Skinflats/Carronmouth max 86 on 7 Jan, 78 on 11 Feb, 9 on 14 Mar &, last, Pr on 13 Apr; 1 on 26 Aug, 25 on 2 Nov & 52 on 20 Dec. More than usual at Kinneil: 51 on 16 Feb, last 7 on 25 Feb; 1st autumn on 24 Aug, max 57 on 23 Oct (MVB GO AB DMB DT).
S   M Lecropt 3 Feb to 28 Apr, displayed to F Mallard (DT MVB CJM).

Area Summary

Jan	Feb	Mar	Apr	-	Aug	Sep	Oct	Nov	Dec
92	130	42	7		3	1	74	29	52

The high estimate in Feb probably reflects movement between Skinflats & Kinneil: no simultaneous counts available.

SHOVELER *Anas clypeata* (p)
F   Kinneil: Pr from 1 to 20 Jan, M on 11/30 Mar; 1 on 27 Jul, 3 on 24 Aug, max of 7 on 15 Sep & 9 on 31 Oct, last 6 on 22 Dec. Skinflats: Pr 8-12 Apr, M on 29th; 1 on 24 Aug, 4 on 14/16 Sep, last 1 on 27 Nov. (MA DAC DT GO AB).
C   4 (2M) Cambus Pools 27 Apr (AT).

POCHARD *Aythya ferina* (W)
> WEBS max: 154 inland in Jan, 137 in Dec (NB).

F   Autumn return 2 Kinneil & 8 Skinflats on 7 Oct (DT MA) – no reports from elsewhere.

C   30 Gartmorn 22 Dec (AT).

S   34 L.Ard 18 Jan & 21 on 17 Dec. 33 Lake of Menteith 8 Jan & 48 on 14 Dec. (NB). 28 Carron Valley Res 13 Jan & 13 on 3 Nov. 17 L.Walton 15 Dec (DAC). 1st of autumn 8 Blairdrummond 8 Sep (DOE).

TUFTED DUCK *Aythya fuligula* (B,W)
> WEBS max: 446 inland in Jan, 555 in Dec (NB).

F   32 Black Loch 6 Nov (NB). 24 L.Ellrig 16 Dec (JN). Max 22 Skinflats 3 Mar, last 2 Prs on 29 Apr. 2 on 5 Jul. 8 Kinneil 29 Apr; 7 on 24/27 Jul, 5 on 7 Oct. (GO DT AB).

C   169 Gartmorn 14 Jan & 163 on 9 Nov (AT). 30 Cambus (on Forth) 10 Feb (DAC). 4 Blackdevon mouth 29 Jul (CJH).

S   70 Coustry 16 Oct. 106 Lake of Menteith 24 Oct & 114 on 14 Dec (NB DAC). 40 Cambusmore 6 Aug (PWS). M Ashfield 18 Jun (DP). 4 Prs Blairdrummond 12 Jun, 60 on 8 Sep (DOE).

SCAUP *Aythya marila* (w)
F   Kinneil: F on 27 May & 8 Jul, Pr on 16/17 Jun, 1 or 2F 3-27 Jul; 5 on 21/23 Oct, 10 on 22 Dec. Skinflats: F from 14 Feb to 10 Apr, 3 (2M) on 13 Apr, 2 on 14 Aug. F Carriden 21 Oct. (DMB GO DT AB).

S   M Gart 31 Oct (DAC).

*EIDER *Somateria mollissima* (w)
F   Blackness: 4 (3M) on 1 Jan, 6F on 8 Jul & 8F on 22nd (MA). 2M Kinneil 18 Feb, 3(2M) on 1 Apr & 4 on 4 May, 2F on 17 Jun; 3(2M) on 2 Dec. 8(6M) Carronmouth 8 Apr. (DT GO AB).

*LONG-TAILED DUCK *Clangula hyemalis*
F   Skinflats: F on 19/20 Jan; F on 21 Oct & 2F on 29th (GO AB MVB).

S   2M Lake of Menteith 17 Nov & F on 16 Dec (NB DAC).

BLACK SCOTER *Melanitta nigra*
F   5 Kinneil 23 Oct & 4 on 11 Nov (DT).

GOLDENEYE *Bucephula clangula* (W)
> WEBS max: 44 Forth Estuary in Jan & 72 in Dec (DMB). 631 inland in Jan, 571 in Nov (NB).
> Few summering birds & late autumn return – first on 6 Oct, F at Carron Valley Res..

F   Max at Skinflats 41 on 10 Feb, 20 on 7/8 Apr (last 5 on 21st), 20 on 31 Oct & 41 on 16 Dec (AA GO MVB). 25 Kinneil 23 Oct (DT). 50 Carronshore-Larbert 16 Dec (AB MA). 14 Black Loch 29 Jan (NB).

C   31 Alloa Inches 11 Nov. 57 Gartmorn 1 Jan & 41 on 9 Nov (DMB AT). 103 on lower Devon (Tillicoultry to Cambus) in Jan, 45 in Dec (GEL KW PD). 6 (1M) Devonmouth 27 Apr (last), F on 30 Jun & 3/16 Aug (DAC AT).

S   Pr +2Y L.Tay 30 May (PWS). 130 on Forth, Forthbank-Stirling 13 Jan, 55 on 11 Nov (AT). 65 Lake of Menteith 14 Feb (last 3 on 29 Apr), 107 on 17 Nov. 40 L.Venachar 17 Dec. 55 L.Dochart/Iubhair 16 Feb (still 30 on 30 Mar); 70 on 17 Dec (NB DOE PWS). 33 Carron Valley Res 13 Jan. Last Kippenmuir (F) on 25 Apr (DAC). 3M summered Blairdrummond (DOE).

*SMEW *Mergus albellus* (w)
S   M L.Tay (Killin) 11 Jan; M L.Dochart/Iubhair on 18/30 Mar & on 17/19 Dec (PWS NB).

RED-BREASTED MERGANSER *Mergus serrator* (B,W)
46 Forth Estuary in Jan & 63 in Oct (DMB).
F   Skinflats: 16 on 6 Feb, 5 on 7 Apr; 14 on 15 Sep & 34 on 16 Dec (MVB GO AS).
29 Kinneil 21 Oct & 50 on 11 Nov (DMB).
C   31 Kennetpans 18 Feb & 14 on 14 Oct (AT CJH). M on Devon at Tullibody 17 Feb
& 14 Mar (KW).
S   Pr on Allan at Ashfield 18 Apr (DP). Autumn inland records: 4 Cambusmore 22
Sep, 5 Airthrey Loch 7 Oct, 1 Doune Ponds 21 Oct (PWS MK AD).

GOOSANDER *Mergus merganser* (B,W)
WEBS max: 125 inland in Feb, 83 in Dec. 22 on estuary in Sep (NB DMB). 1st Ms
in autumn were in November, 1 Skinflats on 2nd, 6 Airthrey on 17th & 4
L.Katrine on 22nd (AB RJ NB).
F   Late bird Skinflats 1 Jun, then 1 on 28 Aug to max 37 on 10 Sep (AB GO). 19 on
Carron below Denny in Jan (AB MA). 14 L.Ellrig 18 Feb (JN).
C   R.Devon: 16 Dollar-Tillicoultry 18 Sep (DE).
S   25 on Forth, Forthbank to Teith 14 Jan & 27 on 11 Feb, 20 Cambuskenneth 3 Mar
(MB AT DAC), no other river counts above 11. 26 Airthrey 11 Mar & 24 (16M) on
7 Dec (DMB MVB). 12 Carron Valley Res 3 Nov & 15 N.Third Res on 10th (DAC
BO). On R.Teith: In Jun F+3J at Doune on 9th, 3 Prs at Forth confluence on 16th;
19 F/J at Lanrick 28 Jul (JNW AS DOE). F+8Y Carron Valley Res 8 Jul (AKM).

RUDDY DUCK *Oxyura jamaicensis* (w)
No records.

RED KITE *Milvus milvus*
The RSPB/Scottish Natural Heritage re-establishment scheme continues with a
max winter roost of 49 on 13 Jan. Twelve AoTs, two with single birds one of
which was poisoned. Nine pairs attempted clutches, seven pairs raised 17Y. 6
birds (German origin, ex illegal captive birds) released. (DOE). Please try to note
wing tag colours on any bird you may see.
Many reports Braes of Doune included 25 together 25 Jan, 35 at roost on 28th,
but max was 49 on the 13th. 20 at roost 13 Sep & max of 50 on 28 Nov. During
Nov, 62 individuals identified by wing tags, included 5 from the Black Isle. (CJM
DSK DOE). At Lecropt 1 on 10 Feb stooped (unsuccessfully) at Rooks & on 31
Dec 1 took meat from factory despite pursuit by Crows (DP CJM). 1
Cambusmore 16 Mar & 8 Apr, Torrie 16 Sep (DAC PWS BB). 1 Thornhill 5 Feb to
4 Jun (JS SS). 1 Flanders Moss 25 Jan & 1 Lake of Menteith 24 Feb & 8/16 Apr (DP
DAC).

HEN HARRIER *Circus cyaneus* (b, w)
19 males and 16 Ringtails noted, omitting repeated records.
F   1 Kinneil 10 Feb (DMB). M Castlecary 25 Nov (MA).
S   Pairs & singles on Carse of Stirling 6 Jan to 4 Mar and 6 Oct to 30 Dec. Also about
15 distinct records on surrounding hill ground & Strathallan, M Carron Valley
(W) 6 May (GJB). Pairs bred successfully Braes of Doune & Sheriffmuir (DOE).
Regular on Flanders Moss Jan/Feb & Jun-Nov. (SS JS DJC DT MVB DOE DP MA
DAC NB).

SPARROWHAWK *Accipiter nisus* (B,W)
Many records (ca 65) throughout area, mainly Jan-Apr & Sep/Dec. Caught
Starling at roost Polmont on 22 Sep & Fieldfare Braes of Doune on 10 Dec. 1 took
a Knot at Kinneil 30 Mar, then robbed by Crow. Chased House/Tree Sparrows at
feeding site Thornhill Carse in Nov & M found as collision death on 19 Dec (JW
DJC GO). Few noted in midsummer when it is presumably secretive. 2 prs
Doune 21 Apr & 1 Pr Lanrick 3 May (DOE). Raised 2Y Skinflats (GO AB).

BUZZARD *Buteo buteo* (B,W)

As breeding bird: widespread S & C, breeding regularly & generally more frequent F.

F   Pr with Juv by Carron west of Larbert, Pr + Juv SW of Falkirk; 6 over Camelon 16 Sep (MA). At Torwood all year (AB). 2 Wallacebank Jan/Feb (AS). At Skinflats-Bo'ness Jan -Apr & Aug-Dec, max 5 Kinneil 25 Aug & 5 Skinflats 10 Oct; 5 over Polmont 7 Oct (DT GO AS JW).

C   3 Alloa Inch 28 Apr (DMB).

S   12 Prs found Menteith to Braes of Doune (about 1 pr per sq km); 10 pr checked & raised 27 Y (DOE). Large groups in breeding range were 5 Blairdrummond 31 Jan, 7 Airthrey 11 Mar, 10 Doune 21 Apr, 8 Buchany 27 May, & 9 Argaty 27 Aug. Food pass seen G.Meann on 22 Aug. (NB DMB DOE DJC).

GOLDEN EAGLE *Aquila chrysaetos* (b,w)

S   8 territories checked, 6 occupied by pairs & 1 by a singleton, also signs of prescence on the last. Only 4 of the pairs were successful, reared 5Y (PSA). 1 in W. Ochils 31 Dec (DP).

OSPREY *Pandion haliaetus*

S   Ten pairs attempted 9 clutches, 8 pairs raised 21Y. One young bird fledged prematurely, taken into care and then released. Male of one pair identifed as a 6 year old bird, probably from an Argyll nest (DOE).
1st of year on 30 Mar (DT), many reports from 13 Apr. Summer records from Carron Valley Res from 24 May to 20 Sep, max 8 on 15 Jul (JNW GJB RKP DMB). 1 Killin 2 Jun, 1 -> S Lecropt 5 Aug (PWS DT). Last at Flanders Moss 4 on 22 Aug (DP).

KESTREL *Falco tinnunculus* (B,W)

Difficult to make significant observations, hence generally under-recorded.

F   Pr raised 2Y Skinflats (AB GO). Pr + 3Y Camelon (AB). Noted 13 sites Mar/Jul (AS).

S   Pr + 4Y Buchany (DOE), Pr+ 1Y Abbey Craig (JNW).

MERLIN *Falco columbarius* (b?,w)

F   F Skinflats 2 Mar (GO).

S   Singles Hill o'Row (M) 27 Jan, Sheriffmuir 30 Mar, Lecropt 11 Nov; F near Gart 30 Jun (MVB AB DT).

PEREGRINE *Falco peregrinus* (B,W)

F   2 Kinneil 7 Jan; 2 Skinflats 11 Mar & 16 Aug, then 1 to 1 Oct. M Polmont 29 Sep & Imm Letham 11 Oct (DMB GO JW AB).

S&C   16 territories checked, 13 pairs. All 13 pairs successful, reared 28 Y (minimum, PSA). 6 records Flanders Moss Jan/ Feb & Oct. M Doune 7 Feb & 1 Dec (SS DP DOE).

RED GROUSE *Lagopus lagopus* (B,W)

Generally under-recorded.

S/C   Noted on Dumyat & Alva Moss in Dec (MA).

S   19+21 Ballochleam (Gargunnocks) 9 Sep (JNW). 3 sites at Finglas 27 Mar & 4 fence deaths G.Meann 6 Apr. F+6Y G.Kendrum 18 Jun (DJC).

*PTARMIGAN *Lagopus mutus*

S   2 B.Dubchraig 28 Oct (DP). M Ben Ledi 9 May & 1 on 17 Oct (DJC M.Griffin). 6 Juv Ben Lomond (poss. Clyde) 15 Aug (AE).
2000: 10 Meal Glas & 10 Sgiath Chuill (Dochart hills) 28 Oct (J Gordon).

BLACK GROUSE *Tetrao tetrix* (B,W)

S   Leks with 6, 6 & 5 Ms at L.Katrine, L.Arklet & G.Casaig (DJC). Also recorded at Duke's Pass, L.Walton, Earls Hill, Tyndrum & Ardeonaig (L.Tay). (DAC DP JNW PWS). 4F Carron Valley (W) 28 Nov (RKP). Hybrid M Black Grouse/Capercaillie, as 1999 & 2000, G.Finglas 19 Aug (DOE).

CAPERCAILLIE *Tetrao urogallus*
S   no records received

GREY PARTRIDGE *Perdix perdix* (B,W)
Coveys increase going east from the central carse of Stirling into Falkirk.
F   9 Kinneil 7 Oct (DT). Max Skinflats 10Y on 22 Jul, 15 (13 Juv) on 27 Aug & 14 on 19 Dec (MA AB GO). 16 on landfill near Carron dams 16 Sep, 17 Camelon & 12 Bonnybridge on 14 Oct, 20 Camelon 4 Nov & 12 Howierig 28 Oct (MA).
S   6 Thornhill Carse 19 Jan & 10 on 2 Dec. 13 Lecropt 10 Dec (DJC DAC). 30 on rough pasture Claylands (Kippen) 17 Nov – possibly released birds (DT).

QUAIL *Coturnix coturnix*
S   2M calling Thornhill 9 Jun (SS).

PHEASANT *Phasianus colchicus* (B,W)
Abundant (usually by releases) on fields next to keepered estates.
F   Through year Skinflats

WATER RAIL *Rallus aquaticus* (w)
F   Skinflats: 3 on 28 Jan, 2 from 19 Apr, copulation 24 Jun, 2 Juv on 31 Aug, last on 1 Nov. 1 Kinneil 28 Jan, 18 Feb, 22 Sep (DT AB GO).
C   1 Marchglen 7 May (AT). 1 Cambus Pools 30 Jun, 29 Sep & 16 Dec (DAC CJH). 2 Tullibody Inch 20 Jun, from 15 Aug to 7 Oct, max 3 on 28 Aug (MVB DMB).
S   1 L.Watston 16 Nov (CJH).

MOORHEN *Gallinula chloropus* (B,W)
WEBS max: 103 inland in Jan & 174 in Oct (NB).
F   12 Kinneil 7 Oct (DT). Max on Union Canal Polmont-Avon 29 on 11 Nov (JW PD). 16 on Forth-Clyde canal Grangemouth-Bonnybridge 14 Jan. 18 Callendar Park 16 Jan & 25 on 15 Oct (DMM AA).
C   10 Cambus Pools 29 Sep. 2 AoT Blackdevonmouth 29 Jul (CJH).
S   At Killin marshes from 26 Apr to 22 Jun (PWS). Probably bred 9 other sites (JNW DP et al).

COOT *Fulica atra* (B,W)
WEBS max: 323 inland in Jan & 470 in Dec (NB).
F   20 Callendar Park 16 Jan (AA). Bred Skinflats (AB GO).
C   Ad+4Y Blackdevonmouth 29 Jul (CJH). 99 Gartmorn Dam 14 Jan, 205 on 22 Dec (AT).
S   33 Airthrey 12 Feb (MK), only 3 prs in Jun (AT). 137 Lake of Menteith 8 Jan, 144 on 14 Dec. Nest in gullery Ashfield 18 Jun (DP).

OYSTERCATCHER *Haematopus ostralegus* (B,W)
132 on Forth Estuary in Jan & 137 in Sep (DMB).
Apart from 4 Lecropt on 27 Jan, spring return inland in mid-February: Lecropt 10th, Craigforth & Doune 11th, Ashfield & Kippen Muir 18th, Gart & Coustry on 20th, Killin 26th (DT MVB DOE DP DAC NB PWS). Still on breeding ground Airthrey 26 Jul (CJH).
F   105 Blackness 7 Jan & 235 on 1 Dec; 85 Kinneil 28 Jan, 80 on 16 Sep. (MA AS DT).
S   4 AotT in 1.2 Ha Doune, 4 AoT Ashfield, 7 AoT G.Finglas Res (KMG DP DJC). In Feb: 175 Craigforth on 11th, 120 Blairdrummond on 20th (DT NB).

RINGED PLOVER *Charadrius hiaticula* (b,W)
17 Forth Estuary in Feb & 17 in Oct (DMB).
F   23 Bo'ness 10 Jan. 31 Kinneil 17/18 Feb. 21 Skinflats 9 Jun, 20 on 19 Aug (AS DT GO).
S   Pr Cambusmore 16 Mar (PWS). 2 Aot Finglas Res 16 May (DJC).

GOLDEN PLOVER *Pluvialis apricaria* (B,W)
No breeding records. 182 on Forth Estuary in Jan & 1206 in Dec (DMB).

F   Blackness: 120 on 26 Aug & 202 on 11 Nov. Skinflats: 132 on 17 Feb, 1st return 13 on 19 Jul, 105 on 28 Sep, 585 on 21 Oct & 265 on 4 Nov. 1206 Kinneil 9 Nov, only 350 on 24th, 600 on 2 Dec (MA GO AB MVB DMB DAC DT).

S   119 Thornhill Carse 4 Nov (DT).

GREY PLOVER *Pluvialis squatarola* (W)

F   Scarce on estuary. Skinflats: 1st return 17 Aug, 19 on 1 Oct & 21 on 7th (GO AB MA). 2 Blackness 16 Apr (MA).

LAPWING *Vanellus vanellus* (B,W)

    1120 on Forth Estuary in Feb & 2856 in Sep (DMB).

F   250 Blackness 12 Aug (MA). Kinneil: 500 on 18 Feb, 400 on 1 Apr; 2 pr nested; 80 on 3 Jul & 170 on 20th, 440 on 25 Aug, 820 on 16 Sep, 1050 on 11 Nov. Skinflats: 590 on 11 Feb; 22 on 22 Jun, 150 on 3 Jul, 300 on 15 Aug, 1020 on 16 Sep, 920 on 21 Oct & 508 on 16 Dec (DT AB MVB DMB *et al*).

C   750 Tullibody Inch 31 Jul, 1500 on 15 Aug & 1200 on 7 Oct. 130 Alva 3 Nov (CJH MVB DMB GEL).

S   Spring return: 500 Lecropt 11 Feb. AoTs in Apr/May: 7 (5 in 1.2 Ha) Doune Ponds, 5 Hill o'Row, 4 Blairdrummond, 10 Cxallander (Bracklinn) (KMG DOE). 150 Cambuskenneth 12 Aug., 330 Thornhill Carse 21 Oct, 50 Lecropt 29 Dec. 30 on Drip Carse 30 Dec followed plough (JNW DAC CJM).

KNOT *Calidris canutus* (W)

    2400 Forth Estuary in Feb & 3500 in Dec (DMB).

F   2400 Kinneil 10 Feb; first adult 24 Jul, Juv on 16 Aug; 75 on 23 Oct & 3000 on 9 Nov (DMB DT). 1300 Bo'ness 10 Jan & 1700 Blackness on 1 Dec (AS). Very few Skinflats, incl. 1on 3 Jun & 1st of autumn on 3 Aug (AB GO).

*SANDERLING *Calidris alba* (p)

F   2 Skinflats 11 May (GO).

*LITTLE STINT *Calidris minutus*

F   1 Skinflats 11 May (v.scarce in spring) & 1 Kinneil on 6/7 Oct (GO DMB DT).

CURLEW SANDPIPER *Calidris ferruginea* (p)

F   Skinflats: 2 Ad on 20/21 Jul, then imm – 2 on 2-16 Sep, 3 on 1 Oct & 2 on 6th. Kinneil: 1 on 31 Aug, 2 on 6 Oct & 1 on 23rd (DT GO MA MVB DMB).

    Area Summary (half monthly)

Jul	Aug	Sep	Oct
0 2	0 1	2 2	5 1

DUNLIN *Calidris alpina* (b?,W)

    7200 Forth Estuary in Feb & 9015 in Dec (DMB).

F   5500 Kinneil 10 Feb & 5500 on 9 Nov. Skinflats: 4750 on 7 Jan & 3510 on 16 Dec; 185 on 8 Apr & last of spring 12 on 3 Jun, return from 30 Ad on 20 Jul & 80 (incl. Juvs) on 26th; 720 on 21 Oct, 6900 on 12 Dec (DMB MVB DT AB).

RUFF *Philomachus pugnax* (p)

F   Skinflats: first of autumn 5 Aug, sharp max 10 on 24th & 23 on 26th Aug, last on 15 Sep. 2 Kinneil 22 & 31 Aug. (GO MA AB DT).

C   12 Tullibody Inch on 2 Sep (DMB).

    Area Summary (half monthly)

Aug	Sep
3 25	17 1

JACK SNIPE *Lymnocryptes minimus* (w)

F   3 Skinflats saltings 3 Mar. Kinneil: 1 on 10 Feb; 2 on 23 Oct, 4 on 11 Nov, 3 on 2nd Dec & 5 on 26th. 1 Grangemouth 21 Oct (GO DMB DT).

C   3 on Devon at Alva 19 Jan (GEL).

S   1 on Forth by tide limit 14 Jan (MB). 1 Thornhill 7 Apr (SS). Flanders Moss: 1 on 25/30 Jan; 3 on 25 Oct, 2 on 16 Nov & 1 on 18 Dec (DP). 1 Lecropt 27 Jan & 2 on 16 Dec (DT). 1 on upper Forth 20 Dec (JNW).

SNIPE *Gallinago gallinago* (B,W)
   Probably under-recorded in breeding season but may have decreased (Ed).
F   Max Kinneil only 9 on 18 Feb & 12 on 11 Nov (DT). 10 Skinflats on 20 Jan, 15 on
       25 Sep & 12 on 30 Dec (AB MA). 15 St Helen's Loch 6 Nov & 26 on 2 Dec (NB).
C   21 Marchglen 27 Jan (AT). 12 on Devon at Gogar 15 Jan (KW). 23 Tullibody Inch
       7 Oct (DMB). 11 Blackdevonmouth 1 Dec (CJH).
S   Lecrop: 27 on 21 Jan & 31 on 18 Feb; 13 on 15 Aug & 59 on 22 Oct (DT MVB).
       18 on Forth at Frew 31 Oct (DR). 1 site Flanders Moss in Apr & 2 in Jul (DP).

WOODCOCK *Scolopax rusticola* (B,W)
       Under-recorded (Ed).
       Roding in Mar-Jun at Torwood (4), Lake of Menteith, Dunblane (AB DT MVB).
       Nests found at Plean CP (3Y), Brig o'Turk (C/4), G.Finglas (later predated); (AS
       DAC DJC). Recorded from Lake of Menteith to Falkirk at 7 sites Jan/Feb and 8
       in Nov/Dec. 4 in woodland patch at Viewforth (Stirling) on 8 Mar (JNW) –
       spring passage ?

BLACK-TAILED GODWIT *Limosa limosa* (W)
F   The max site count was 114 Kinneil 23 Oct (Forth estuary total 132). 40 to 50
       birds wintered Jan-Dec, numbers decreased from late Feb except for a brief
       increase (spring passage?) in late Apr, then there were few until late Aug. The
       only records from sites away from Grangemouth were 2 at Cambus on 27 Apr
       & at Tullibody Inch, 14 on 30 Sep & 7 on 7 Oct. (DT GO AB DMB MVB)

Site Summary (half monthly)

	Jan	Feb	Mar	Apr	May	Jun	Jul	Aug	Sep	Oct	Nov	Dec
Knnl	29 24	41 7	5 17	19 8			2 2	18 90	90	35 114	50	18
Skn	1 20			15 55	1 6	3	13 1	5 11	22 21	36 25	100	28

BAR-TAILED GODWIT *Limosa lapponica* (W)
       252 Forth Estuary in Jan & 101in Dec (DMB).
F   84 Blackness 7 Jan. Kinneil: 250 on 7 Jan, 130 on 18 Feb; first of autumn 3 Jul, 20
       on 16 Sep & 100 on 23 Oct. 17 Skinflats 16 Sep (MA DT DMB MVB).
C   1 Tullibody Inch 30 Sep & 7 Oct (DMB).

WHIMBREL *Numenius phaeopus* (p)
F   In spring from 24 Apr (2->NW) to 12 May, max 3 on 10 May. First of autumn, 1
       Skinflats on 4 Jul; max 11 ->W (also 9 Kinneil) on 24 Aug, last on 31st (GO AB
       DMB DT).
C   1 Tullibody Inch 14 Jul (DMB).

Area Summary (half monthly)

Apr	May	Jul	Aug
2	3	2 4	1 11

CURLEW *Numenius arquata* (B,W)
       570 on Forth Estuary in Jan & 735 in Sep (DMB).
F   54 Bo'ness 25 Jan (AS). 490 Skinflats 7 Jan; 40 on 3 Jul, 400 on 21 Oct. 350 Kinneil
       3 Jul & 520 on 8 Aug. (MVB DT). 137 Lathallan Pond 16 Dec (JW).
C   120 Tullibody Inch 9 Dec. 141 Inch of Ferryton 16 Dec (CJH).
S   Spring return Thornhill 9 Mar, 10 Carron Valley Res on 10th, 40 Lecrop on 31st.
       1 AoT G.Finglas & 2 AoT Thornhill (W.Moss-side). 23, early flocking, Sheriffmuir
       12 Jun. (SS DAC DT MVB DJC).

SPOTTED REDSHANK *Tringa erythropus* (p)
F   Kinneil: 2 wintered 12 Jan to 28 Apr, fed in wake of Shelducks on 20 Jan. 1 on
       16 Sep, last on 7 Oct. 1 Skinflats 28 Aug (GO DT DAC DMB AB).

REDSHANK *Tringa totanus* (B,W)
       1574 Forth Estuary in Feb & 2037 in Oct (DMB).
       First spring return 13 February at Kildean, then in March: R.Devon & upper
       Forth on 12th, Gart on 16th, Kippen Muir on 21st, Killin on 30th (GEL RC NB

DAC PWS).

F 123 Bo'ness 10 Jan (AS). Skinflats: 305 on 7 Jan, still 250 on 8 Apr; 75 on 3 Jul, 585 on 16 Sep & 653 on 16 Dec. Kinneil: 250 on 8 Apr; 75 on 3 Jul, 1345 on 16 Sep (MVB DT DMB). Wintered on lower Carron, max 7 on 14 Jan (MA IH).

C 103 Kennetpans 16 Dec (CJH).

S Spring return Cambusmore 16 Mar, Kippen Muir 11 Apr & Doune 15 Apr (PWS DAC DOE). However, an estimated 600 at L.Tay (Killin) on 4 Apr (PWS) was unprecedented and presumably indicates a fall of migrants en route for Iceland from east coast estuaries.

GREENSHANK *Tringa nebularia* (p)

F Skinflats: 1 Jan to 12 Mar; autumn from 2 Aug (max 11 on 19 Aug & 8 on 30 Sep), 1 from 14 Nov to 19 Dec. At Kinneil 22 Aug to 27 Sep, max 2 on 19 Sep. (AB GO MA DMB MVBDT).

C 2 Alloa Inches 2 Sep & 1 on 7 Oct. 2 Blackdevonmouth 1 Sep & 2 on 7 Oct (AT DMB). 1 Kennetpans 21 Oct (CJH).

S 1 Flanders Moss 21 Aug (DP).

 Area Summary (half monthly, autumn passage)

Aug		Sep		Oct		Nov	
1	12	12	11	7	3	4	1

GREEN SANDPIPER *Tringa ochropus* (p)

F Wintered on Carron (Larbert), 1 on 16 Mar & 26 Dec (MA). 1 Kinneil 8 Jul (DMB). 1 on Avon at Avonbridge 27 Jul (AS). 2 Skinflats 31 Aug & 16 Sep, 1 on 16 Nov & 16 Dec (GO MVB).

C Wintered Blackdevonmouth, 1 on 13 Feb & 19 Dec; 1 on 6/7 Oct (CJH DMB).

S 1 on Allan at Ashfield 25 Oct (AW).

COMMON SANDPIPER *Tringa hypoleucos* (B)

 Spring return in April: 13th at Ashfield & 14th at Dunblane widespread by 30th (DP MVB).

F Skinflats: first of autumn 3 Jul, max 3 from 3 Aug to 2 Sep, last 2 on 4 Sep. Kinneil from 20 Jul to 4 Sep, max 9 on 24 Jul & 22 on 22 Aug (DT GO AB). 1 AoT on Carron at Camelon from 28 Apr, Pr with Juv on 7 Jul (MA).

S 9 on Allan at Dunblane, A9 to M9, 29 Apr (MVB). 11AoT G.Finglas Res 16 May (DJC). 12 Lecropt 7 Jul (DMB).

 Passage autumn totals :

	Jul		Aug		Sep	
	13	14	5	25	3	0

TURNSTONE *Arenaria interpres* (W)

F 13 Grangemouth 13 Jan, 14 Bo'ness 1 Apr. 3 Carriden 9 Nov, 15 Blackness 1 Dec (MVB DMB AS).

*ARCTIC SKUA *Stercorarius parasiticus* (p)

F Kinneil: 3 on 3 on 9 & 22 Sep, 2 on 24th & 1 on 7 Oct. 1 Blackness 11 Nov (DT MA GO).

*GREAT SKUA *Catharacta skua*

F 1 Skinflats 26/27 Sep. 1 Kinneil 10 & 27 Sep. (GO DT).

*MEDITERRANEAN GULL *Larus melanocephalus*

S Adult in winter plumage at Skinflats 20 Dec, with other gulls then flew inland (GO AB). *2nd record for area Ed.*

BLACK-HEADED GULL *Larus ridibundus* (B,W)

F 1000 Blackness 7 Jan. Post breeding assembly of 40 at Skinflats on 22 Jun, 540 on 2 Sep (MA AB).

C 500 Kennetpans 18 Feb (AT). 525 by R.Devon at Gogar 21 Sep (KW).

S 75 following plough Drip Carse 30 Dec (CJM). 50 at Ashfield colony 18 Feb, 40 nests (no eggs yet hatched) on 18 Jun, left on 26 Jul. Flanders Moss colony abandoned (DP).

COMMON GULL *Larus canus* (B,W)
F   413 Slamannan 3 Oct & 1028 (2nd highest count for area) on 6 Nov (NB).
S   10 AoT G.Finglas Res 16 May (DJC). 250 following plough Drip Carse 30 Dec (CJM).

LESSER BLACK-BACKED GULL *Larus fuscus* (b,S)
        More mid-winter records (9, 18 birds) than usual. Spring arrival probably represented in February by 1 at Forthbank on 9th, 1 St Helen's Loch & 5 Skinflats on 10th, & 1 at Stirling on 16th; in March 1 L.Dochart on 6th & 10 Camelon on 7th (CJH AA DJM PWS MA).
F   1 Bonnybridge & 3 St Helen's Loch 15 Jan. 1 Larbert 14 Jan & 35 on 16 Sep. 50 Skinflats 26 Jul & 59 on 2 Sep. 610 at estuary roost, Skinflats, 9 Oct. 4 L Ellrig 16 Dec. 2 Kinneil 22 Dec. (AA MA GO AB JN).
C   1 Kennetpans 16 Dec (CJH).
S   1 Carron Valley Res 13 Jan. 147 Thornhill 24 Oct & 34 L.Coulter 6 Nov. 4 L.Coulter 2 Dec & 1 Lecropt on 16th   (DAC NB DT).

HERRING GULL *Larus argentatus* (b,S,W)
        No records this year !

GREAT BLACK-BACKED GULL *Larus marinus* (S,W)
        Highly under-reported.
F   170 Kinneil 1 Jan & 19 on 26 Dec (MA GO). 90 Higgins Neuk roost flight 3 Nov (CJH).
C   47 Alloa Inches 29 Dec (CJH).
S   Inland record: 6 (5 Ad) L.Coulter 2 Dec (NB).

KITTIWAKE *Rissa tridactyla* (P,w)
F   Mainly adults: 7 Kinneil 1 Apr, 12 on 22 Aug & 18 on 2 Dec (DT). 6 Bo'ness 22 Dec (MA).

SANDWICH TERN *Sterna sandvicensis* (P)
F   2 Skinflats 22 Jun, to 36 on 17 Aug & 122 (15 parties) ->W on 18th; last 8 on 7 Oct (AB GO MA). 15 Kinneil 10 Aug & 50 on 22 Sep (DT). 150 Carriden 16 Sep (DMB).
S   6 over Thornhill 19 Aug (SS) – nb Skinflats passage on 18th.

COMMON TERN *Sterna hirundo* (B)
F   lst, 1 Kinneil 29 Apr, 50 Skinflats 4 May; last 4 Kinneil 11 Sep (DT AB). 78 nests Grangemouth Docks 27 May then 81, with many well grown chicks, on 27 Jun; still 8 nests with chicks on 24 Aug. Best overall estimate of 86 nests (12 on cairns by R.Carron) & at least 23 chicks raised, possibly 50. (DMB). Max 58 feeding on Skinflats pools in Jun (GO) presumably come from Grangemouth colony.
S   1 Coillechat quarry (Braes of Doune) 16 Jun, possibly breeding (DOE). 1 'Comic', prob this sp., Gart 17 Oct (NB CJH).

BLACK TERN *Chlidonias niger*
F   1 Ad in moult Skinflats 24 Aug (MA). 25 Kinneil 6 Oct, in tight flock (DMB) – record count for area.
S   1 Gart Loch 17 Oct (NB CJH) – 2nd inland record since Carron Valley Res on 2 Oct 1983.

GUILLEMOT *Uria aalge* (W)
F   55 Kinneil 18 Feb (DT) but few elsewhere though 2 S.Alloa 10 Mar & 1 on 11th were far up the Forth (DMB JNW). In autumn a few Kinneil/Skinflats Sep-Nov, small influx in Dec with 20 Kinneil on 2nd & 26 Skinflats shore on 16th, when 46 on whole estuary (DT MVB) – see C & S records.
C   5 Kennetpans & 14 Cambus 16 Dec (CJH). 1 on Devon at Gogar 19 Dec (KW).
S   1 Airthrey 20 Nov (MVB). 1 L.Katrine 17 Dec (NB).

FERAL PIGEON *Columba livia* (B,W)
> No significant observations, note that some birds do not have white rumps and could be mistaken for Stock Doves.

STOCK DOVE *Columba oenas* (B,W)
> Widespread in small numbers, surely much overlooked.

F   10 Skinflats 28 Jan & 19 on 30 Apr; 11 Bonnybridge on 14 Jan. 18 Kinneil 9 Sep, 17 Camelon 31 August & 30 on 4 Nov (DT GO MA).

C   14 S.Alloa "bridge" 29 Dec (CJH).

S   10 Plean CP 10 Feb & 11 Lecropt on 11th (DT)

WOODPIGEON *Columba palumbus* (B,W)
> Greatly under-reported.

F   139 Skinflats 12 Apr (GO).

S   300 Blairlogie 8 Jan & 650 on 9 Feb (CJH). 500 Keir 22 Oct (DJC). 1000 Lecropt 11 Nov (DT). 700 Kinbuck 24 Feb & 1000 on 4 Dec (NB MVB).

COLLARED DOVE *Streptopelia decaocto* (B,W)
> Greatly under-reported. Scarce away from suburbs and large farms.

S   2 Killin 26 Feb to 7 Sep (PWS). 30 Lecropt 7 Jan (DT).

CUCKOO *Cuculus canorus* (B)
> First record 25 April, L.Venachar (DJC); then in May: Daldorn on 2nd, Braes of Doune on 5th, G.Lochay on 7th, Flanders Moss on 10th (DOE DT DP).

S   Juv in Aug G.Finglas & Flanders Moss (DJC DP).

BARN OWL *Tyto alba* (b,w)
F   1 Falkirk 2 Nov (MA).

S   Pr reared 2Y in barrel nest, Flanders Moss (DP). Also, through year, 6 sites on Carse of Stirling, 2 Braes of Doune, 1 Callander, Ruskie, L.Venachar, Ashfield (DAC CJH JS SS DJC).

TAWNY OWL *Strix aluco* (B,W)
> Reported 9 sites: Gartmorn, Tillicoultry (2),Torwood, Dunblane, Braes of Doune (2), Strathyre, L.Katrine (AT AB DJC DSK). 1 fledged Dunblane 25 Jun (DP).

*LONG-EARED OWL *Asio otus* (b,w)
F   1 Skinflats 28 Sep (GO).

C   1 Cambus Pools 21 May (AT).

S   1 Earlsburn Res 8 Sep (DOE). 2 Carron Valley (W) 12 Jun (GJB).

SHORT-EARED OWL *Asio flammeus* (b,W)
> Remains very local, possible breeding only in Trossachs and Gargunnock Hills.

F   Best year for a long time. Skinflats: 1 on 17 May – unusual date; 1 on 28 Sep then regular with max of 2 on 9 & 31 Oct, 4 on 16 Nov, last 1 on 16 Dec (GO AB MVB). 1 Kinneil 24/25 Aug, then from 7 Oct to 2 Dec with 3 on 24 Nov (DMB DT DAC).

S   1 Earl's Hill/Cringate 20 Apr & 7 May (JNW DT). Pr Carron Valley (W) 12 Jun (GJB). 1 Sheriffmuir 18 Jul (DSK). 1 Finglas 24 & 27 Jul & 18 Sep (DJC MR).

SWIFT *Apus apus* (B)
> First record Camelon 28 Apr (MA). In May: 1 Falkirk on 1st, on the 2nd at Callander, 3rd Thornhill, 5th at BoA, widespread from 8th; lst at Killin not till 14th (AB DJC SS CJH PWS). Typical last dates were in Aug – Dunblane on 15th, Stirling 16th, Doune 21st (NB JNW DOE), but 35 Bo'ness on 28th were unusual (AS).

F   130 Bo'ness 31 Jul (AS). 200 Skinflats 1 Aug (AB).

S   100 Flanders Moss 7 Jul. Max over Dunblane 40 on 6 Jul & BoA 35 on 3 Aug, but 120 Lecropt 6 Aug & 100 Craigforth on 15th. (DP JNW CJH DT).

NIGHTJAR *Caprimulgus caprimulgus* (b?)
> No records this year

KINGFISHER *Alcedo atthis* (b,w)
> Recorded throughout but only 3 records Apr to Aug – probably reflects WEBS

activity.

F 5 dates on Carron below Denny Jan/Feb & Sep-Dec, max 3 Larbert W 14 Jan. 1 Bonnybridge (F/C Canal) 4 Oct, 1 on Union Canal at Maddiston 28 Nov (MA PC PD).

C 1 R.Devon at Cambus 20 Apr & 30 Jun (AT DAC), 7 records Jan & Sep-Dec up to Tillicoultry (KW GEL PD). 1 Blackdevonmouth 8 Sep; 1 Gartmorn on 21 Oct & 22 Dec, 1 Alloa 8 Dec (AT NB).

S 2 Doune 6 Aug (bred) (DOE). On Allan: at BoA 15 Sep & 13 Oct (CJM MVB); at Ashfield 13 Sep to 28 Dec (DP DSK). 1 Thornhill 4 Aug (JS). 1 Gart 16 Oct & 6 Dec; 1 on Balvag above Strathyre 7/8 Sep & 7 Oct; 1 L.Doine 7 Oct (DJC NB).

GREEN WOODPECKER *Picus viridis* (B,W)

Widespread Stirling.

C 12 records through year, Alva Woodland Park to Dollar Glen (AT).

S Recorded, mainly Mar to Jul, at 12 sites L.Ard Forest – Doune – Plean CP (DOE DAC NB MVB DP AT JNW). 1 Killin 14 Nov (PWS). 1 Carron Valley (W) 15 Mar (RKP). Juv at Stirling 13 Sep fed on ants (RJ).

GREAT SPOTTED WOODPECKER *Dendrocopus major* (B,W)

F 1 Skinflats 27 Jan, 21 Oct & 28 Nov (AB MVB GO). 1 Bo'ness, Bonny Water & Wallacebank Wood in Jan, 1 Larbert 16 Dec (MA AS).

S Reported 14 sites mainly Feb to Jul, from L.Ard Forest north to Strathyre & east to Plean CP (JNW DAC SS DSK CJM). 1 Fintry 11 Feb (DAC) – sole record for Gargunnocks.

SKYLARK *Alauda arvensis* (B,W)

Singing Lecropt 28 Jan (CJH).

F 80 Skinflats 8 Feb (AB).

S 104 Blairlogie 9 Feb. 170 Lecropt 10 Feb, 90 on 1 Dec (CJH MVB). 120 Thornhill Carse 12 Nov, 100 on 24th & 300 on 11 Dec (DJC SS).

SAND MARTIN *Riparia riparia* (B)

First records on 30 March, 3 Larbert & 6 Lake of Menteith (MA DT). In April: 1 Lanrick & Doune on 1st, 2 Airthrey & 15 Carronshore on 2nd, 200 Lake of Menteith on 7th, 1 Skinflats on 8th, 4 Ashfield & 47 Barbush on 10th (DOE DMB AB DP MVB). Last 50 Killin 9 Sep (PWS)

S Nesthole counts in May/Jun: 622 Cowiehall, 85 Laigh Hills, 530 Cambusmore, 60 L.Doine (JNW NB). 1 at G.Finglas 1 May repeatedly landed on track to catch spiders (DJC).

SWALLOW *Hirundo rustica* (B)

First records in April, rather late: 2 Lake of Menteith on 7th, 1 Carronshore on 13th, 2 Menteith Hills on 14th, 10 Blairdrummond & at Thornhill on 16th, then widespread (DOE AB DT SS). Last 15 Doune on 21 Sep & 3 Cambus Pools on 29th (DOE CJH).

F 20 -> E at Skinflats 25 Aug & 2 Sep (GO).

S In Aug: 100 Aberfoyle on 8th, 300 (roost) Tullibody Inch on 15th & 700 (with House Martins) Lanrick on 25th (DAC MVB DOE).

HOUSE MARTIN *Delichon urbica* (B)

Arrivals in April, 1st 20 at BoA on 6th (before Swallows) & 40 Doune on 7th (CJM DOE); main arrival after 26 Apr, not at Killin till 14 May (PWS). Typical late dates were 60 Doune on 21 Sep & 110 Airthrey on 27th, last 2 Airthrey on 9 Oct (DOE MVB DMB).

S Arrived at BoA colony 5 May – four weeks after first seen in area (CJH).

TREE PIPIT *Anthus trivialis* (B)

First at Doune 15 Apr (DOE), then Queen Elizabeth FP 29 Apr; in May: Thornhill on 1st, G.Lochay on 5th, Alva on 7th (MVB SS DT AT).

S   3 AoT Flanders Moss (DP).

MEADOW PIPIT *Anthus pratensis* (B,W)

Relatively scarce midwinter: 16 Blairlogie 8 Jan & 65 on 9 Feb, 14 Skinflats 8 Feb (CJH AB). Spring return 104+70 G.Finglas 27 Mar (DJC).

F   40 Skinflats 16 Oct (AB).

*ROCK PIPIT *Anthus petrosus*

F   3 Kincardine Bridge to R.Carron 3 Mar (GO). 1 Blackness 30 Dec (MA).

GREY WAGTAIL *Motacilla cinerea* (B,w)

7 January records, 3 on lower Carron. 5 in Dec from 5 sites (AB DSK DP AS DSK). 1 Killin 26 Feb suggests spring return (PWS).

3 AoT Invertrossachs; nest c/5 G.Finglas, all fledged; nest in house porch Lochearnhead (DOE DJC). Bred in BoA at least 500 m from a burn.Foraged on roofs in Polmont & Braes of Doune & on pavement in BoA (CJH JW DSK).

PIED WAGTAIL *Motacilla alba* (B, w)

Noted at only 9 sites in Jan (CJH JNW AT DOE DAC).

F   White Wagtail M.a.alba : 1 Airth 4 Jun (GO) –*late date, Ed.*

S   Roosting on and in Stirling Station: 65 on 14 Jan & 50 on 21 Mar; also 80 on roost flight 4 Oct (DOE JNW).

1 AoT Laighills (NB).

WAXWING *Bombycilla garrulus*

The influx of Dec 2000 continued strongly into this year. 14 flew W at Kinbuck 2 Jan & 20 to SW over Airthrey on 8th. Highest numbers were in Jan, especially around Falkirk & Stirling with largest single flocks of 64 Polmont on 9th & 33 Lecropt on 6th; possibly totals of 153 in Bo'ness-Grangemouth-Falkirk area and 78 around Stirling. Apart from 41 Tillicoultry 7 Mar, the only Clacks reports were 3 Menstrie on 6 Jan & 2 Gartmorn on 7th. Numbers declined rapidly around Falkirk through Feb though there were 37 at Polmont 11 Mar & 2 Apr. However, around Stirling flocks stayed on with 35 as late as 26 Mar. The last record was of a pair at Dunblane on 8 Apr. Cotoneaster berries were widely reported as favourite food, birds also seen to take grit or salt from pavement (MVB JW MA AD CJM AT ACH et al).

The only end of year report was 4 on Rowans by Falkirk bypass on 6 Dec (GO).

DIPPER *Cinclus cinclus* (B,W).

Widespread song in Jan.

F   1 on Avon at Grangemouth (Jinkabout Bridge) 20 May, 1 nearby on 17 Sep (JW AS) – presumably marks limit of breeding range.

C   15 on Devon, Tillicoultry-Dollar, in Jan; 20 in Dec; also at rivermouth (Cambus) Feb (DE DAC).

S   3 AoT on Teith at Lanrick 3 May (DOE). Pair on Allan at Ashfield raised 2Y (DP). On R.Teith: 15 Daldorn-Wester Row (5 km) in Jan; 11 Doune – Daldorn (5 km) in Feb (RAD DOE MW).

WREN *Troglodytes troglodytes* (B,W)

Widespread and common, few records.

S   4 AoT Laighills (NB).

HEDGE SPARROW *Accentor modularis* (B,W)

S   Trio at Stirling, song from late Jan and display 25 Feb, often chased by Robin (CJM). 5 AoT along Forth at Cambuskenneth 25 Mar (JNW).

ROBIN *Erithacus rubecula* (B,W)

Under-recorded.

S   9 close together near birdtable at Strathyre 2 Jan, ice & snow on ground (DJC). 1 AoT Laighills (NB).

REDSTART *Phoenicurus phoenicurus* (B)

        1st of spring at Thornhill 30 Apr, then Rhuveag 3 May & Flanders Moss on 11th (SS DT DP).

S   6M Port of Menteith 21 May (DOE). 29 prs Trossachs colony (38 in 2000) reared 75 (HR). Pr with 2Y Braes Killin 6 Jun (PWS).

WHINCHAT *Saxicola rubetra* (B)

        First of spring 1 Kinneil on 29 Apr (DT). In May: G.Finglas & Thornhill on 1st, Braes of Doune (4M) on 5th (DJC SS DOE). Last of autumn 1 Skinflats 3 Sep (AB).

S   5 AoT Flanders Moss (DP). 3 sites Braes of Doune with 4 family parties Lundie 21 Jun (DOE).

STONECHAT *Saxicola torquata* (b,w)

F   At Skinflats from 28 Jan to 8 Mar, max 3 on 15 Feb. 1 Skinflats & 1 Grangemouth (S) 26 Dec (DT GO AB). 3 Kinneil 11 Nov & M on 24th (DMB DT DAC).

C   Pr Cambus Pools 22 Dec (DAC).

S   In breeding season noted at Earl's Hill, L.Arklet, G.Finglas, Flanders Moss (5 AoT), Callander. Pr feeding 5 Juv at Brig o'Turk & family at G.nan Meann 25 Sep (DJC DT DP MR). In winter/autumn at 4 further sites, Carron Valley Res (Pr+2J 6 Oct), Lecropt, Sheriffmuir, Braes of Doune. (DAC DT DOE).

WHEATEAR *Oenanthe oenanthe* (B)

        First record 1 Kinneil 9 Apr, 5 G.Meann on 6th, 1 Thornhill on 7th; on estuary to 29 Apr (DT DJC SS). Autumn migrants on estuary regular to 19 Sep, 1 Skinflats 1-7 Oct & 1 Kinneil on 7th (MA GO).

S   Only other records from breeding range were on Braes of Doune & Gargunnocks (DOE JNW).

*RING OUSEL *Turdus torquatus* (b)

S   F G.Kendrum 26 May; 6M along ridge, B.Each to B.Vorlich, 10 Jun (DJC DP). In G.Finglas 1 Meall Wood 21 Sep and 20 (feeding party) G.nan Meann on 27th (MR) – last record the largest group ever recorded locally.

BLACKBIRD *Turdus merula* (B,W)

F   10 by Carron at Dorrator 25 Mar (MA) – possibly migrants?

S   lst fledgling at Callendar on 3 May (DJC). 5 AoT Laighills (NB).

FIELDFARE *Turdus pilaris* (W)

        April departure marked : 90 Ashfield on 8th, 80 ->N Slamannan on 18th, 180 Fintry on 19th, 42 ->W Dunblane on 22nd; last was 1 Skinflats on 29th (MVB NB DAC GO).

        1st of autumn were in October, 17 ->SW Kinbuck on 13th, then 400 Flanders Moss & 430 L.Arklet on 17th, widespread thereafter. Large flocks in November, notably on 4th Nov with 1000 Lecropt & estimated 10,000 in 5 km north of Gargunnock–Kippen road; these must have moved on rapidly since max later flock was 330 Kinbuck on 28 Nov & 2 Dec (MVB DP NB ABM).

F   62 Bo'ness 19 Jan was only sizeable winter flock (AS).

C   100 ->NW Cambus Pools & 103 ->W Kennetpans 21 Oct (CJH).

S   500 Flanders Moss 3 Feb & 150 Blairlogie on 9th (DOE CJH). Noted feeding in gardens at Dunblane & Stirling during snow in late Feb & early Mar (NB CJM).

SONG THRUSH *Turdus philomelos* (B,W)

        Few in January – 2 Kinneil , singles at Blackness, Bo'ness & 4 sites Falkirk-Bonnybridge (MA). Song widespread from mid February (CJM DAC DP JNW).

S   5 in Dunblane garden during snow on 2 Mar (NB). 2 AoT Ashfield and 3 AoT along c500 m of railway line at Stirling (DP JNW). 5 AoT Laighills (NB).

REDWING *Turdus iliacus* (W)

        First of autumn 4 ->SW Dunblane 26 Sep; in Oct: 16 ->W Dunblane & 5 Keir on 5th; widespread from 10th & then large flocks: 1500 Thornhill Carse & 300 L.Laggan on 19th, 1000 Lecropt on 22nd. Largest Nov flock 125 on 24th (MVB DMB DJC NB DT).

C   100 Dollar 1 Jan (AT). 100->NW Cambus Pools & 60 ->W Kennetpans 21 Oct (CJH).

S   120 Arnprior 7 Jan (DAC). 100 Lecropt 4 Feb, 100 Airthrey 4 Mar & 4 (last) 2 Apr (MVB). 2 resident in Stirling garden Jan & Feb (CJM).

MISTLE THRUSH *Turdus viscivorus* (B,W)

Greatly under-recorded.

S   1 AoT Finglas in May (DJC). 1in Dunblane garden (deep snow) 1 Mar – lst for 6 years (NB). 51 Sheriffmuir 22 Sep (AT).

GRASSHOPPER WARBLER *Locustella naevia* (b)

F   1 Skinflats 29 Apr & 14 May (GO).

C   1 Marchglen 27 Apr & 7 May; 1 Cambus Pools 8/21 May (AT).

S   5 sites, song 11 May to 26 Jul, Flanders Moss, last on 19 Aug (DP SS DOE). 1 Stirling (Millhall bing) 11 May (JNW).

SEDGE WARBLER *Acrocephalus schoenobaenus* (B)

1st record Fallin 30 Apr. In May: 3 Skinflats on 1st, Ashfield & Thornhill on 8th, Kinneil on 9th. Last were 2 Skinflats 10 Sep. (DMB AB DP SS DT GO).

C   4 AoT Marchglen 7 May (AT).

S   4 AoT Blairdrummond 20 May, 1 Bannockburn School pond 5 Jul (DOE JNW).

WHITETHROAT *Sylvia communis* (B)

First records in April: Thornhill 26th, Skinflats 30th. 2 Kinneil 4 May & 1 Skinflats on 6th. Last Skinflats 17 Aug. (DOE GO DT AB).

F   First fledged young at Skinflats 22 Jun (AB).

S   3 AoT Laighills 23 May (MVB). 2 AoT in scrub on outskirts of Stirling 6 Jun (JNW).

GARDEN WARBLER *Sylvia borin* (B)

First records in May: Doune on 3rd, 3 Dunblane-Ashfield on 12th (DOE MVB DP). Last at Airthrey 23 Aug (DMB).

F   2 AoT Polmont Woods 20 May (JW).

S   4 AoT Doune Ponds & 1 Blairdrummond in May (KMG DOE).

BLACKCAP *Sylvia atricapilla* (B)

Winter records: 1 Strathyre 2 Jan. In Stirling gardens: M 2 Jan to 18 Feb &, nearby, F on 20 Jan & max 2 M & 2F from 14 Feb to 23 Mar (DJC RJ CJM). Birds fed on cotoneaster berries, peanuts, peanut cake, seed, & bread; unafraid of other species. M Stirling 11 Oct & M Dunblane 9 to 12 Dec, fed on apples (DSK). M at BoA 2 Apr possibly overwintered, further spring arrivals not till Doune on 15th & Lake of Menteith on 16th (DMB DOE DAC). 1 in song Skinflats 1 May was unusual site (AB).

F   2 AoT Polmont Woods 20 May (JW).

S   3 AoT Lanrick 12 May (DT). 5 AoT Blairdrummond 20 May (DOE).

WOOD WARBLER *Phylloscopus sibilatrix* (B)

Underrecorded

First record Dunblane 29 Apr – on passage (MVB). Then 1 Brig o'Turk & L. Venachar 1 May & 4 Glen Lochay on 7th (DJC DT).

S   2 AoT Port of Menteith & 1 AoT Lake of Menteith in May (DOE). 4 AoT Aberfoyle 30 Jun (KMG).

CHIFFCHAFF *Phylloscopus collybita* (B)

First records in March: Airthrey on 20th, Blairlogie 24th, Plean CP & Larbert on 31st; widespread from 4 Apr (DMB DAC DT MA).

F   Migrants at Skinflats 1 & 7 Apr (GO). 1 Camelon 4 Jun (MA).

S Song heard Invertrossachs (2), Doune (2), Dunblane (2), Ashfield (2),Stirling (1), Plean CP (3) (DOE MVB DP CJM DT).

WILLOW WARBLER *Phylloscopus trochilus* (B)
  First records in April: Ashfield on 9th, Cambus on 13th, Dunblane & Lake of Menteith on 16th, Airthrey on 17th; widespread from 20th (DP AT DOE DMB et al). Last of autumn1 Stirling 9 Sep (CJM).
S 18 AoT in 1.5 km Dunblane 29 Apr (MVB). 24 AoT Laighills (NB).

GOLDCREST *Regulus regulus* (B,W)
  Under-recorded. In gardens Jan to Mar at Bo'ness, Carronshore & two sites Stirling, fed at birdtables & on lawns (AS AB RJ CJM).

SPOTTED FLYCATCHER *Muscicapa striata* (B)
  Seems scarce –"only one seen all summer", only ten reports in all.
  First records in late May: Doune on 25th, Strathyre on 29th & L.Venachar on 30th (DOE DJC).
S 2 AoT Lendrick. Adult(s) & young seen Aberfoyle, Buchlyvie, R.Teith at Lanrick (DJC DAC DOE).

PIED FLYCATCHER *Ficedula hypoleuca* (b)
  First record was a pair nest building at Finglas 1 May (DJC). 2M G.Lochay 7 May (DT).
S At Trossachs colony 18 prs reared 65 Y (HR). 11 prs (7 successful) at G.Finglas boxes reared 31Y (DJC).

LONG-TAILED TIT *Aegithalos caudatus* (B,W)
F 6 Bo'ness 17 Jan & 18 on 9 Oct (AS).
S 2 came to nuts at Stirling through Mar, 6 on 23 Sep (RJ). 11 Dunblane 1 Jan, 30 Flanders Moss on 1 Feb & 11 Strathyre 6 Nov (NB DP DJC).

COAL TIT *Parus ater* (B,W)
  Widespread but no notes received.

BLUE TIT *Parus caeruleus* (B,W)
  Under-recorded.
C First young fledged Dollar 24 Jun (AT).
S First young fledged BoA 17 Jun (CJH). 4 AoT Laighills (NB).

GREAT TIT *Parus major* (B,W)
  Under-recorded.
S lst song at Stirling 28 Jan (CJM). AoT Laighills (NB).

TREECREEPER *Certhia familiaris* (B,W)
  Under-recorded (Ed). Only records were 2 in mixed tit flock Lake of Menteith 17 Nov (NB) & singles in gardens at Bo'ness in Jan & (lst record) Grangemouth in Nov; also 1 at Skinflats (where it is a rarity) 15 Feb & 4 Sep (AS GO AB).

GREAT GREY SHRIKE *Lanius excubitor*
S 1 in middle of Flanders Moss 25 Jan (DP), 1 on north edge of moss 29 Jan to 11 Feb (JS). 1 Carron Valley (W) 2/13 Feb (GJB).

JAY *Garrulus glandarius* (B,W)
F 2 Wallacebank Wood Jan-Feb, Nov (AS). Through year at Torwood (AB).
C At Alva Woodland Park Jan/Feb, May; 2 Harviestoun 9 Dec & 2 Gartmorn 21 Oct (AT).
S Recorded 27 sites, mainly in Trossachs, from L.Chon and L.Doine east and south to Callander, BoA and Plean CP; Buchlyvie was only site south of the Carse of Stirling. Max 5+2 L.Ard 27 Dec (NB DAC DSK DP).

MAGPIE *Pica pica* (B,W)
  Abundance around Stirling is not usually noted in the west, now large groups widespread in Falkirk.
F 25 Bo'ness 6 Jan & 9 Dec. 16 Bonnybridge 10 Jan & 30 Camelon 8 Feb. 11

Skinflats 7 Dec (MA AS GO).
S   16 Fallin 19 Jan (NB). 42 Airthrey roost (with Jackdaws) 22 Dec (AT).
JACKDAW *Corvus monedula* (B,W)
    An overlooked species, about 5 reports.
F   19 Skinflats 14 May – unusual here (GO).
C   150 Tullibody Inch 31 Jul (CJH).
S   24 Plean CP 17 Feb (AB). 350 BoA p.m roost flight 23 Dec (CJH).
ROOK *Corvus frugilegus* (B,W)
S   Rookery counts: 7 colonies at Dunblane totalled 290 nests, largest at Holme Hill (157); top four rookeries accounted for 90 % of total (MVB). Main colonies at BoA not counted, new sites at Fountains Rd (5) & by A9 at Airthrey (4) (CJH). 360 Blairlogie 9 Feb. 1200 on Airthrey roost flight 22 Dec (CJH).
CARRION CROW *Corvus corone* (B,W)
S   Hoodies: Noted in Feb & Oct-Dec at 8 sites in the usual breeding range (L.Katrine-G.Lochay), max 4 G.Dochart 19 Dec (NB DAC). 1 paired with Carrion Crow at Finglas (DJC). Hybrids at Lecropt 30 Sep & L.Katrine 17 Dec (MVB NB).
RAVEN *Corvus corax* (B,W)
S   13 territories checked, 12 pairs. 7 successful pairs of which 5 raised 13 Y; Pine Marten predation suspected for one of failures (PSA). 8 Strathyre 9 Jan (DJC). 3 records in W.Ochils in Dec (MA). Outwith of main breeding areas: Max 3 Thornhill 2 Feb & Doune 1Dec, 10 occurrences Flanders Moss, Dunblane, Lecropt, mainly Jan/Feb & Nov/Dec but 1 over Dunblane 12 Aug & display at Daldorn 12 May (DOE SS DP MVB DT).
STARLING *Sturnus vulgaris* (B,W)
    Greatly under-reported.
F   1500 at Kincardine Bridge roost 3 Nov, roosted at 17.00 (CJH).
C   3000 at Tullibody Inch roost 15 Aug (MVB).
S   350 Thornhill Carse 19 Oct (DJC).
HOUSE SPARROW *Passer domesticus* (B,W)
    Under-recorded.
S   45 Blairdrummond Carse 8 Sep (DOE). Record 300 at feeding site Thornhill Carse on 1 Dec (DJC).
TREE SPARROW *Passer montanus* (B,W)
    Widely reported in small numbers from Thornhill eastwards.
C   12 Kennetpans 14 Jul (AT).
F   9 Camelon 7 Jan (MA). Singles at Skinflats in Jan, 6 on 10 May – unusual date (AB GO)
S   In breeding season at Lecropt & Kildean (DT DP). Few Lecropt Jan/Feb but 25 on 22 Oct & 45 on 1 Dec (DT MVB). 30 Thornhill Carse 15 Jan & 20 Blairdrummond Carse on 28th (NB DSK). Coordinated census on Carse of Stirling on 6 Jan gave total of 122. At feeding site on Thornhill Carse 41 on 6 Jan & 70 on 18 Dec (DJC).
CHAFFINCH *Fringilla coelebs* (B,W)
S   500 Kinbuck 11 Nov & 2 Dec. 230 Doune 27 Jan & 300 on 2 Dec. 350 Lecropt on 2 Jan & 150 on 1 Dec 400 Lanrick 7 Apr & 500 (on grazed kale) Callander 4 Dec. (MVB DOE DJC). 200+250 Flanders carse 30 Nov & 300 Thornhill 18 Dec (DP DJC). 20 AoT Laighills (NB).
BRAMBLING *Fringilla montifringilla* (W)
    Very local in spring , some large flocks in autumn.
C   150 in stubble Alva 8 Dec (NB).
S   70 on beech mast Callander 7 Apr, last 15 on 26th. 6 Lecropt 22 Oct; none later

on Carse of Stirling but large influx in northeast of area in November with 300 Doune on 10th (in uncut oats) & 1000 Kinbuck on 11th – only 70 on 24th (DOE DT MVB).

GREENFINCH *Carduelis chloris* (B,W)

Under-recorded.

S 150 Lecropt 26 Aug & 120 on 4 Nov. 150 Doune 25 Nov (DT MVB DOE). 1 AoT Laighills (NB). Immature bird was window casualty at Stirling 7 Mar (CJM).

GOLDFINCH *Carduelis carduelis* (B,W)

F 34 Skinflats 31 Aug (GO). Pr Polmont, collecting spider's webs on 20 May (JW).

S 4 AoT Laighills (NB). 40 Flanders Carse 2 Oct & 20 on 30 Nov. 50 Doune 25 Nov (DP DOE). Fed on nuts Jan – Jun at Buchlyvie & Stirling (DAC RJ).

SISKIN *Carduelis spinus* (B,W)

Only record of garden feeding from Stirling, especially Jan-Feb (RJ).

S 53 L.Venachar 18 Jan. Song flight at Dunblane 8 May. 50 Callander 9 Nov & 100 Killin on 21st; 130 Carron Valley Res 15 Dec & 45 L.Dhu on 17th (NB PWS DAC).

LINNET *Carduelis cannabina* (B,W)

F 180 Kinneil 7 Oct. 500 Skinflats 28 Jan, still 150 on 8 Apr; 800 on 21 Oct (DT MVB).

S 300 Hill of Row 27 Jan. 550 Lecropt 27 Jan, 180 on 30 Sep, 1200 on 4 Nov & 400 on 1 Dec (MVB). 115 Blairlogie 9 Feb (CJH). Widespread in Braes of Doune, max 60 Lanrick 7 Apr, 150 Argaty 17 Nov & 150 Doune 2 Dec (DOE). 50 Thornhill 25 Sep (SS). Small flocks in two Stirling gardens Oct & Dec, fed on birch seeds (JNW RJ).

TWITE *Carduelis flavirostris* (b,W) S

F 60 Skinflats 16 Dec & 115 on 30th (MVB MA). 25 Kinneil 9 Nov (DMB).

C 5 Tullibody Inch 25 Nov, roosted in reeds (DMB).

S In May 4 AoT G.Finglas & 1 Glen Lochay (DJC DT). 60 G.Finglas 19/22 Aug (DOE DJC). 230 Lecropt 10 Feb (MVB) – unprecedented flock for Carse of Stirling.

REDPOLL *Carduelis cabaret* (b,W)

S Flanders Moss: Pr on 7 Jun then, 1 km away, F on nest c/4 13 Aug (DP). 11 G.Finglas 5 Jul & 19 Aug (DJC DOE). 6 Killin 3 Feb (PWS). 40 Dunblane 10 Nov, of 5 feeding in garden birch on 22 Dec, one killed by cat (MVB NB).

COMMON CROSSBILL *Loxia curvirostra* (b,W)

F 3 Skinflats 18 Dec (MVB).

S Widespread Jan-Apr from Carron VR to Braes of Doune (Song on 14 Jan), max 15 Carron VR 13 Jan, 6 Torrie Forest 24 Feb & 6 L.Ard Forest 29 Apr. 9 Carron Valley (W) 28 Jan (AKM). Similar pattern Oct-Dec with 13 Callander 9 Oct, & small parties Carron Valley 23 Oct to 15 Dec, max 18 on 15 Dec, & 19 Cambusmore on 16th. (DSK RKP JM DAC DT DOE MVB).

BULLFINCH *Pyrrhula pyrrhula* (B,W)

S 2 AoT Doune Ponds 2 Apr. 1 AoT L.Venachar (Lendrick) 18 Jun (DOE DJC). Fed on buds of apple & amelanchier at Stirling (RJ). 26 in birch scrub Flanders Moss 30 Jan (DP). 10 L.Ard Forest 22 Nov (NB). 9 G.Finglas 24 Jan & 21+4+8 on 26 Dec (DJC DAC).

SNOW BUNTING *Plectrophenax nivalis* (W)

C In Ochils, 38 Colsnaur Hill 2 Dec & 25 Alva Moss on 9th (MA). First Ochils flocks for many years.

YELLOWHAMMER *Emberiza citrinella* (B,W)

F 13 Skinflats 20 Jan (GO). 25 Carron & 60 Bonnybridge on 14 Jan (MA).

C 80 Cambus (partly cut cereal) 8 Feb (CJH).

S In Jan : 30 Ashfield on 2nd, 64 Hill of Row on 14th, 24 Thornhill carse on 15th.

35 Lecropt 10 Feb & 40 Thornhill carse on 11th. 46 Lecropt on 15 Dec (MVB DOE NB). Scarce away from arable farms – 3 Balquhidder 27 Mar & 1 Killin on 7 May (PWS).

REED BUNTING *Emberiza schoeniclus* (B,W)
F   41 Skinflats 1 Mar (GO).
C   35 Cambus (partly cut cereal) 20 Jan (CJH).
S   4 AoT Flanders Moss (DP). 33 Lecropt 10 Feb & 13 on 15 Dec (MVB). 25 Thornhill 26 Jan to 18 Feb (JS).

CORN BUNTING *Emberiza calandra*
         No records this year.

ESCAPED SPECIES

RUDDY/CAPE/PARADISE SHELDUCK *Tadorna ferruginea/ cana/ variegata*
         A bird at Skinflats 2/3 Mar (also seen in Fife) had not quite the right body plumage for a typical *T. ferruginea* and was thought to be possibly a hybrid; a different bird at Gartmorn Dam 16 Sep & 14 Oct was also not really typical (GO AT). In any case, a captive origin is very likely.

BUDGERIGAR *Melopsittacus undulatus*
F   Albino bird at Skinflats 26 Aug, chased by Swallow (DT).

BOOK REVIEWS

The Return of the Natives: the final Review of the Millennium Forest for Scotland Trust. 110pp.

This handsomely produced and well illustrated book is introduced by Prince Charles and by Convenor Barbara Kelly. Director Penny Cousins outlines the background to the initiative and what it has achieved. Woodlands themes, projects, awards, acknowledgments and reflections follow in detail, with facts and figures, and lessons for the future; and a final postscript by the Earl of Dalkeith, the Millennium Commissioner. Eighty woodland restoration projects on more than 400 sites throughout Scotland have secured over 20,400 hectares of native woodland, and 183 kilometres of footpaths. The total value attributed to this is £30 million. Provision has been made for periodic reviews and future needs. In all a notable achievement!

Brophytes of Native Woods: a field guide to common mosses and liverworts of Scotland and Ireland's native woodlands. 40pp. Carol L Crawford, Native Woodlands Discussion Group, 4d New Bridge St., Ayr.

Sponsored by SNH and Eamonn Wall this is available free from the author by sending an A5 sae.

Fauna Britannica: natural history, myths, legends, folklore, tales, traditions. Stefan Buczacki. Hamlyn. ISBN 0 600 59867 5. £40.

Years of research by this noted naturalist/wildlife expert have produced an attractive comprehensive reference guide. It is a celebration of Britain's wildlife past and present, its social and cultural history, habitats, fables and traditions, with taxonomic clssitication and detailed indexing. (Launch date 15/9/02)

Calatria, the journal of the Falkirk Local History Society, has recently had these FNH interest papers –
George Forrest, Botanist: the Falkirk connection, by Brian Watters – in no. 14 (Spring 2000) pp 69-72.
Polerth: the lost dockyard of James IV, by John Reid – in no. 16 (Spring 2002) pp 23-44.

J.A. HARVIE-BROWN (1844-1916), ORNITHOLOGIST
People of the Forth (14)

Ken Mackay

The nineteenth century saw the hey-day of the amateur, often self-taught, naturalist. Stirling and district witnessed several of its citizens rising to national renown on the basis of their painstaking studies and subsequent publications ... Alexander Croall and his Seaweeds, and Robert Kidston with his Carboniferous Plants, to name but two. John Alexander Harvie-Brown made his object of study The Migration of Birds, and was, in fact, one of the founders of research into this mysterious phenomenon.

Harvie-Brown was fortunate in being born into a landed family. His father was proprietor of Shirgarton, near Kippen, and Quarter, near Denny; his mother was heiress to Dunipace House, which in due course became John's favourite abode. He was born on the 27th of August, 1844, in Edinburgh, went to Merchiston Castle School and Edinburgh University, and from there progressed to Cambridge University where he furthered his interest in zoology under Professor Alfred Newton, a spokesman for Natural History in the academic world, a keen ornithologist and indeed one of the founders of the British Ornithological Union. It had been his father's intention for Harvie-Brown to enter one of the learned professions, but his early interest in the world of nature had led him to set his sights on a career collecting specimens for the Smithsonian Institution in Washington. This ambition eluded him, but he maintained voluminous correspondence with a world-wide circle of ornithological friends.

In his late twenties, he and a friend, H.W. Feilden, took part in several European expeditions in search of the breeding grounds of rare birds, including the grey plover and the little stint. They went to Norway in 1871, to Archangel in 1872, to Transylvania in 1874, and to Central Europe in 1875. In those times, a successful bird-researcher had to be an excellent shot and a skilled cragsman to reach and raid the most inaccessible nests. 'What's hit is history; what's missed is mystery,' was their motto. John was reputed to be a first-class shot, though he bore the scars of early mistakes. A second's inattention while charging a muzzle-loader cost him the top joint of his left thumb. On another occasion, a companion's gun went off unexpectedly, peppering his calf with shot and marking him for life.

In 1878, he was invited, along with a number of other gentlemen of the locality, to attend the inaugural meeting of The Stirling Field Club, at which he was appointed a Vice-Chairman, a role he fulfilled for 17 years. He contributed articles to the Club's *Transactions*, including two on *Bird Migration*. He also appears to have supported the Smith Museum's Bird Collection, with locally-shot specimens and birds' eggs.

The systematic study of birds in Britain had only just begun. Identification of rare species relied on the sureness of the observer's aim, a process which hardly ensured breeding success. To conduct a census of the kind organised currently, requires a large number of experienced observers, who were not available in the 1870s. On the other hand, the study of movements of birds crossing our coasts might be possible using an unexpected methodology. The coast of Britain is ringed with a giant chain of lighthouses and light-ships, manned at that time by the disciplined men of the lighthouse service. Migrant birds in their hundreds are regularly attracted to the powerful lighthouse beams, and an appallingly high proportion of them dash to their death in the process. Harvie-Brown hoped to harness the co-operation of those who manned these outposts to keep records of the species and numbers of the fatalities, night by night, and so build up reliable statistics. He also needed dependable colleagues to help process the results.

A first attempt was made in 1879, with Harvie-Brown covering the Scottish lights, and John Cordeaux the English ones. Printed record forms and cloth-lined envelopes (for wings and legs!) were circulated to 100 lighthouses. To their delight, two-thirds of the stations made a return. Harvie-Brown was pleased to recount the story of the lighthouse-man who interpreted his initials as 'John Always Hunting Birds'! The first report was published in *The Zoologist* in May 1880.

The success of this pilot project encouraged Harvie-Brown and Cordeaux to extend their coverage, this time having secured the approval and financial support of the British Association for the Advancement of Science (BA). A directing committee of seven was set up, under the chairmanship of Professor Newton, and including – as well as Harvie-Brown and Cordeaux – a young man who was to make an even greater name for himself, William Eagle Clarke. The number of participating light-houses rose to 126. Eight years of data-gathering required a total outlay of only £175 to cover the general expenses. Each year a full report of the statistics appeared, printed at the expense of the BA.

By 1888 the BA support was wound up, and the task of bringing all the results together was entrusted to Eagle Clarke. In 1912 appeared his two-volume *Studies in Bird Migration*.

Meantime, Harvie-Brown had indulged another ambition. Having enjoyed the hospitality of others who possessed sailing yachts and who invited him to join them in bird-hunting expeditions, he commissioned the building of his own yacht, the *Shiantelle*, built in Fraserburgh in 1887. For 15 years he explored the bird-breeding grounds of the Hebrides, accompanied by friends like Professor Heddle, the geologist, and Dr Eagle Clarke. No doubt he would be adding specimens for his collection, which was housed in his top-floor Museum in Dunipace House. He was also an avid book-collector, and to contain his library he had an annexe added to the House. In due course, this became an extension to the Museum as well.

The Hebridean voyages had another purpose. Harvie-Brown was planning a series of books describing the Vertebrate Fauna of the different regions of Scotland, the first being *Sutherland , Caithness and West Cromarty* published in 1887. His co-author in this and several others was T .E. Buckley. He and his collaborators produced ten volumes in all, approximately one every 2 years ... *The Outer Hebrides* (1888) ... *Iona & Mull* (1890) ... *Orkney* (1891) ... *Argyll & the Inner Hebrides* (1892) ... *The Moray Basin* (1895) ... *Shetland* (1899) ... *The North-West Highlands & Skye* (1904) ... *The Tay Basin & Strathmore* (1906) ... and *The Tweed Area* (1911). It was a great disappointment to him that his own home area of *The Forth* remained unwritten in his day. (It was eventually produced by Misses Rintoul and Baxter about 1935.)

An eleventh volume of the Harvie-Brown series was to have been *The Dee*, co-authored by a George Sim. In the event, Sim decided to publish it independently, which must have caused some heart-burn on the part of Harvie-Brown. His own copy of Sim's *Dee* can be inspected in the Library of the Royal Museum of Scotland. It contains numerous side-notes and footnotes in Harvie-Brown's hand, drawing attention to frequent inaccuracies and inconsistencies in the text!

Harvie-Brown wrote a number of other books on individual species ... *The Squirrel, The Capercaillie in Scotland, The Wonderful Trout,* ... as well as some 250 contributions to learned journals. He was one of the founders of the *Annals of Scottish Natural History*, which developed into *The Scottish Naturalist.* A prolific author, he wrote at great speed though with clarity. In 1900, he broke his right wrist and was faced with an unwelcome halt to his output. His reaction was to buy a typewriter, a novelty in his day, and he was soon typing away happily with his left hand.

He had already shown that he had the strength to overcome disaster. In 1897, his home – Dunipace House – caught fire, and much of his museum collection of bird-skins and eggs was destroyed. Fortunately the Library extension was spared, along with a few hundred skins, the overflow from his main collection. (These specimens, along with his diaries and his Natural History Library, were bequeathed to the National Museum in Edinburgh, where they can still be examined.)

Honours and responsibilities came his way. He was a J.P. for Stirlingshire. He was a Fellow of two Zoological Societies, of London and of Scotland. He was elected a Fellow of the Royal Society of Edinburgh. A long-serving member of the British Ornithologists' Union, he was proud of his Honorary Life Membership of the American Ornithologists' Union. In 1912, the University of Aberdeen awarded him an LLD for his services to Natural History.

Health problems reared their heads. For some years a sufferer from asthma, he had an attack of flu in 1899 which he had difficulty in overcoming. This led to a lessening of his participation in shoots. Less physical exercise meant a gradual increase in his weight, which despite severe dieting, rose to 25 stones. Nothing daunted, he looked around for activities within his abilities. He started to collect soaps, which he would lend for display at fetes and sales of work, in aid of comforts for troops on the Western Front. Another collecting phase was devoted to agates and polished rock specimens. After his death in 1916, the agate collection was offered to the Smith Museum in Stirling , but owing to the building being in the hands of the War Office, it was not accepted.

He passed away on the 26th of July 1916 after a short illness, and was laid to rest beside his parents in the old graveyard beyond Dunipace House. The House, rebuilt after the fire, has disappeared almost completely, but the gravestone with its brief, factual inscription survives. As a pioneer in the field of ornithology, Harvie-Brown's work is still widely quoted and respected. His life-history deserves to be better known. So much of his original material and his diaries and correspondence are available through the Royal Scottish Museum, that full justice may yet be done to the memory of this Great Man of the Forth.

Further reading:

McNaughton, J. 1936. John Alexander Harvie-Brown, LLD, FRSE ... *Transactions of Stirling Natural History & Archaeological Society*, 58, pp 50-63.

Allen, D. E. 1978. *The Naturalist in Britain. A Social History*. Penguin. pp 207-223.

Berry, W. 1948. Some Recollections of J.A. Harvie-Brown and W. Eagle Clarke. *The Scottish Naturalist*, 60, pp 93-98.

Pitman, J. 1983 The J.A. Harvie-Brown Papers (Catalogue). MSS in Royal Scottish Museum, part 3, 90pp. Edinburgh.

THE PRESENT STATUS OF SCOTLAND'S RAREST BUTTERFLIES
in memory of John Berry, Scottish naturalist extraordinary and
lepidopterist for all seasons

David Spooner

The lepidopterist and novelist Vladimir Nabokov wrote (Boyd and Pyle, 2000, 529) that he could never distinguish between the aesthetic pleasure a butterfly gives, and the scientific task of identifying it. Butterflies with their sensitivities to climatological and geophysical data offer much information about the state of the planet, being so immediately responsive to change. Warmer autumns and winters have resulted in a proliferation of scrub and grasses (Bowles 2001, 128 and 2002, 210), while foot-and-mouth disease in 2001 reduced the suitability of many habitats due to lack of grazing.

Consideration of Scottish butterflies can begin with the **Chequered Skipper** (*Carterocephalus palaemon*), a butterfly that is mainly confined to Scotland despite attempts to re-establish it in England, where it died out in 1976 and where viable breeding is still doubtful. Remarkably this Skipper was only discovered in Scotland in 1939 in a region centred on Fort William in oak woodlands on the flood plain of the River Lochy. The Scottish Wildlife Trust undertook a number of surveys in the 1970s uncovering many new localities, at which point the Nature Conservancy Council extended monitoring, and finally Butterfly Conservation came up with a comprehensive Species Action Plan. It is now known in some 50 locations, all in the north west of Scotland, and is relatively stable. It is a Red Data species in Britain and classified as a vulnerable species in Europe, despite its recent expansion in Hungary and Italy.

The major threats to the Chequered Skipper are overgrazing of larval habitats, and dense scrub leading to a shading of adult habitats. As the *Millennium Atlas of Butterflies* puts it:

"Although the distribution appears stable in Scotland, there are serious concerns about the changing management of the butterfly's woodland edge habitats. Increased browsing by deer is preventing the regenerating of native woodland in many areas and several recent forestry initiatives include the fencing of woods against deer. Although this encourages natural regeneration of trees, it can lead to the rapid loss of open space, including breeding areas of the Chequered Skipper. This situation is known to be adversely affecting the butterfly at a number of sites, including some nature reserves. Greater effort should be made to incorporate the needs of insects that require open spaces into such schemes, possibly by introducing some rotational clearance of woodland and maintaining open spaces in potential breeding areas (Asher et al 2001, 55)."

The caterpillars of the Skipper require areas on flushed soils and scrub, while the adult looks for the richer peat sites. The lower poorly drained peat is unsuitable for larvae, and the tree line soon obscures adult flight paths. The larvae need open grassland dominated by the food plant purple moor-grass

(*Molinia caerulea*), growing on wet but not waterlogged soil with bog-myrtle (*Myrica gale*) and birch. (In England it was found on false-brome (*Brachypodium sylvaticum*)). Adult males require wet tussocky grass and open scrub, while the females look for open bracken, herb-rich meadow areas moving toward bog where the moor-grass is plentiful. The *palaemon* caterpillar wraps itself in the grass during the summer and hibernates during the winter.

There is one generation a year with adults flying from the 3rd week of May until the end of June, occasionally into early July. Eggs are laid singly on the foodplant, and the larvae subsequently live within tubes formed by spinning together the edges of a leaf. These caterpillars have a long gestation period after feeding in November, and recent research shows survival rates are higher where the foodplant remains green into autumn. These grow on exceptionally aerated soils that are rich in nitrogen and deep green. Feeding signs usually occur halfway up the *Molinia* blades, with notches on either side. The larvae activate in April, and pupate without further feeding. On emergence the males are territorial and depend on airspace 3-4 m across. Low vegetation and a number of taller perches are important to maintain high temperatures and clear vision. Females look for large amounts of nectar and may congregate in patches of bugle (*Ajuga reptans*) and marsh thistle (*Cirsium palustre*).

Sheep-grazing and rapid tree growth can very easily lead to local extinction. It has disappeared from Glen Nevis because of over-grazing. As so often, complex biodiversity comes into play, with serious conflicts of species and land-use interests. However joint action is being carried out between Butterfly Conservation and Scottish Hydro-Electric whose coppicing of wayleaves for power lines creates clearings where nectar plants and grasses can grow.

The **Large Skipper** (*Ochlodes venata*) is confined to the south west of Scotland. While it is widespread in England and absent from Ireland, it has a foothold in Ayrshire and Dumfries and Galloway. Speculation that it is spreading eastwards are not borne out by recent observations, but its presence in Scotland is stable. As George Thomson reported in his classic conspectus:

> "Mosses, damp meadows, coastal cliffs, rough grassy slopes and open woodland are the places in which this species may be found. It is fond of feeding from flowers, but more often darts about the low plants, settling with its wings in the characteristic half-open position (Thomson 1980, 65)."

It is univoltine (one brood a year). Adults appear in late May and numbers peak in July. In the sun, males patrol in mid and late morning seeking mates. Earlier in the morning and during the afternoon, the male will perch and await passing females. Eggs are laid singly on the undersides of cock's-foot (*Dactylis glomerata*), and purple moor-grass or false-brome. The caterpillars hide in tubular grass constructions they create by joining the edges of a leaf stalk with silk. They overwinter in this hibernaculum before pupation and emergence in late May.

The **Dingy Skipper** (*Erynnis tages*) is, as its name suggests, quite inconspicuous in its browns and greys. It is the most widespread Skipper in England and Ireland, and has a resemblance to the Grizzled Skipper (*Pyrgus* *malvae*) which is however absent from Scotland. The Dingy Skipper is confined in Scotland to a few colonies in the north east, mainly on coastal dunes between Inverness and Banff such as the Spey Bay SWT reserve, together with separate groupings in Dumfries and Galloway. At present it has no statutory protection though, like other butterflies unsecured in the rest of the UK and the Republic of Ireland, it is protected in Northern Ireland under the Wildlife (N. Ireland) Order (1985). In the north east of Scotland, its habitats are generally dunes and undercliffs, though it has been reported inland in Moray, while in the south west it also flies along woodland tracks, clearings and wastelands. Could there possibly be genetic differences between the butterflies at these distant sites?

Common bird's-foot-trefoil (*Lotus corniculatus*) is the Dingy Skipper's main foodplant. Eggs are laid on the longest shoots of the larger plants in sheltered positions. The caterpillars create a tent by drawing leaves together, and then feed through the summer months, spending the winter in a more elaborate hibernaculum. Pupation occurs in spring within this covering, and the imago emerges during May and flies into June. It can be seen basking in the sunshine, but at night like the moths to which the Skippers are closely related, it will almost wrap its wings around dead flowerheads in a way unique for indigenous butterflies.

There appear to have been some losses since the 1980s, though its numbers are stable overall. Many of the colonies are very small, containing fewer than 50 individuals at their peak. Over-shading by trees and scrub growth are constant threats to its numbers, together with either over- or under-grazing. Natural selection may not be on the side of some of these rare butterflies. The fact is that they are pernickety creatures, and the Dingy Skipper like the rest of the rarities requires stronger statutory protection.

The **Small Blue** (*Cupido minimus*) has a sparse population extending from Hawick in the south with a huge gap until Moray and Angus coastal areas, then running sporadically as far as the northernmost north east coast. The Hawick sites have been continually threatened by overgrown salix, mediocre early summers and sparse plantfood, and are now probably devoid of the butterfly, despite conservation work. It is now an insect of the eastern coast beyond the central belt. There is a single plantfood, kidney vetch (*Anthyllis vulneraria*), and the caterpillars feed inside the flowerheads on anthers and seed. They are, like the Orange-tip young, cannibalistic and eat any younger larvae encountered. Scarcity of the foodplant on a habitat thus soon leads to extinction.

Winter is spent in crevices in the earth or beneath moss. Males tend to group on the edges of breeding grounds on shrubs, and this can be easily observed at the site on Seaton Cliffs in Angus. The *Millennium Atlas* remarks:

> "Both larvae and pupae have structures that attract ants and in continental Europe they are usually tended by ants throughout their development. However, detailed observations in Britain have rarely found ants in attendance, possibly because few native ant species forage high up on the flower-heads. There have been very few

observations of the overwintering larvae and pupae but they are possibly attended by ants (Asher et al 2001, 145-146).

The relationship of *C. minimus* with ants, then, remains open to further investigation. (I was recently an adviser to the U.S. Fish & Wildlife Service, and this symbiotic relation between ant and blue butterfly proved the crux in our rescue of the El Segundo Blue Butterfly (*Euphilotes battoides allyni*) on the dunes by Los Angeles Airport). Although the Small Blue's flight period begins earlier in England, in Scotland it flies anytime between the last week in May through June, the time-span lasting only two weeks. The shimmer of blue is quite distinct despite their smallness, although the female is less suffused with blue than the male. Unlike most other butterflies, colouring is not an effect of pigmentation. Instead light is refracted on scales layered like tiles on their wings.

The Small Blue is listed in Schedule 5 of the 1981 Wildlife & Countryside Act which states

> It is a criminal offence to kill, injure or take the species from the wild; possess any live or dead wild specimen, or any part of, or anything derived from them; sell, offer or expose for sale, or possess or transport for the purposes of sale, whether alive or dead, any wild specimen and parts or derivatives of them; or for anyone to publish or cause to be published any advertisement indicating or suggesting that they buy or sell such things, without a license.

Despite the recent extinction of this butterfly from Dumfries and Galloway and probable extinction at Hawick, the survey in preparation of the 2001 *Atlas* revealed 109 additional 10 km squares since the 1970-1982 survey, including many new ones in Scotland.

The Scotch White Spot is almost the perfect name for what is presently known as the **Northern Brown Argus** (*Aricia artaxerxes*), since it is distinguished from the mainly English plain Brown Argus (*Aricia agestis*) by the white spot in the middle of the forewing, and is a butterfly predominantly of Scotland. As Thomson declared in *The Butterflies of Scotland*, "the Scotch Brown Argus, Northern Brown Argus or Scotch White Spot has the honour of being the first butterfly to be recorded from Scotland in literature (Thomson 1980, 116-117)." Where it occurs in the South, in County Durham, its spot is usually dark brown or black. The situation has, however, recently been complicated by genetic studies on a late flying Argus in South Derbyshire in 1999, which was shown to be a hybridization of the Northern Brown and Brown Argus!

The foodplant of this butterfly is common rock-rose (*Helianthemum nummularium*), usually but not always in lightly grazed sward. Typical sites are rocky slopes, either inland or coastal. While in northern England it usually occurs on limestone pavement and outcrops, in Scotland it also occurs in predominantly neutral or even acidic soils where common rock-rose is able to grow if there is some calcareous influence through weathering or flushing (Asher et al 2001, 157). However these sites, south-facing and sheltered, are always well-drained. Of 13 colonies studied in 1986, only 3 were found on calcicolous grassland, 4 being neutral and 5 acidic (Clunas 1986). Thomson observed that the species appeared in the second week of July on the east coast of Scotland as opposed to earlier flight in the west (Thomson 1980, 123). However increases in cloud-cover in the west over the past two decades means that the Northern Brown Argus can now be seen as early in the east as in the south-west, which is to say mid-June at Seaton Cliffs. Although its flight is usually over by mid-August, it was recorded by K.P. Bland at Fealar Gorge, west of Braemar on 22nd September, 1997.

Eggs are laid on the upper side of a leaf of *H. nummularium*, where they are clearly visible and easily counted. They hatch after 6-15 days. The caterpillars do not eat the eggshell, but move to the underside of the leaf where they pierce the epidermis and feed on the interior, leaving the surface intact. They start basking in spring, pupate after the 5th or 6th instar in late May, and while pupating lie on the ground attached to vegetation by silk threads. The pupa hatches after some three weeks. In late afternoon and early evening, small groups of the imago can be seen resting together on long grasses or in flowerheads.

A. artaxerxes had been under-recorded and research for the *Atlas* almost doubled the number of 10 km squares where it was found. It appears in the Borders, along the coast of Dumfries and Galloway, and then has an eastern distribution to south-east Sutherland with strong populations in Perthshire and northern Tayside. Asher and co-authors observe that "it has undoubtedly declined in the south of Scotland, especially in the Borders and around Edinburgh, but further surveys are needed to assess its true status (Asher et al 2001, 158)." However overall it is stable in numbers, even though it is not a highly adaptable insect like the freer flying countryside species. It remains extremely sedentary and so has limited colonizing ability. This Argus requires light grazing of the sward, and where selective spring and autumn grazing has been introduced as it has at St. Abb's Head NNR since 1992, its numbers have increased dramatically.

The **Pearl-bordered Fritillary** (*Boloria euphrosyne*) feeds on marsh violet (*Viola palustris*) in Scotland, but also on common dog-violet (*Viola riviniana*). It is restricted to short, sparse vegetation with a very warm microclimate where the larvae feed on the violets. Temperature must be exactly right among the bracken and leaf-litter (33C) for egg-laying.

Unlike its close relative the Small Pearl-bordered Fritillary (*Boloria selene*), it needs well-drained grassland habitats with decayed bracken, and deciduous woodland. The decline in coppicing has led to an increase in shade and subsequent decline, especially in the south of Scotland. Over the whole of Britain it has declined by 60 % in 30 years. However the re-planting of woods, often with non-native conifers, provided new habitats for the butterfly during the 1950s and 1960s – though even these plantations have now grown dense and shady.

The Pearl-bordered Fritillary requires a mosaic of branches and grass which does not become overgrown, and hence relies on the activity of stock and other animals. Eggs are laid on dead branches and leaf litter. Larvae bask on the litter, and will move many metres for suitable sites and foodplants. In Scotland, *euphrosyne* tends to disperse into metapopulations, similar to the American source-and-sink habitats, often thinly spread over a relatively wide area. The pupae lie in the litter and emerge in late May and June.

There have been other recent losses in Dumfries and Galloway, but in its strongholds in Argyll, the Highlands, west Aberdeenshire and northern Perthshire, it remains stable. As already suggested, there often arises a conflict of ecological interests. The extension of native woodland and the growth of shadow, together with fencing, has entailed a loss of deer grazing to keep the swards short. The prospering of this butterfly – which is especially spectacular in its colouration in Scotland – remains a formidable challenge.

The ecology of the **Marsh Fritillary** (*Eurodryas aurinia*) in Scotland is even more demanding than in England or Wales, generally preferring shorter vegetation. Colonies occur on areas of tussocky grassland dominated by *Molinia caerulea*, and associated with flat areas of *Sphagnum* supporting its abundant foodplant, devil's-bit-scabious (*Succisa pratensis*). The largest colonies are on Islay where grasses are virtually absent and the habitat relatively poor, but where the sites are lightly grazed by sheep or cattle, or both. Over-heavy or under-grazing will not suffice. As a Scottish Natural Heritage Report remarks:

> In Scotland, as in England, *E. aurinia* has declined from the east of the country, and there are extinct sites in Grampian, Inverness, Strathclyde, Glasgow and the Clyde valley, the Borders and Dumfries and Galloway [and we may add Perthshire at Logiealmond and Kinfauns], the majority occurring before 1939. Current known distribution is confined to the Strathclyde region and focussed on the Taynish peninsula, north along the coast to just above Oban and on Lismore, and on the Hebridean islands of Islay, Mull and Jura (Ravenscroft and Gaywood 1996, 3).

It is now extinct in the eastern half of Britain, though I recently visited an introduced colony in Lincolnshire which continues to flourish after some years, and this suggests that a little imagination goes a long way where habitats are propitious for re-introductions.

Eggs can be laid in large batches up to 350 with less in later batches, but they are smaller clusters in Scotland. The larvae are gregarious and spend much of their time in a communal web; these webs are found on shorter scabious rosettes here than in England and Wales. They overwinter in their 4th instar in a small hibernaculum close to the ground, and emerge in late winter or early spring to bask together thus raising body temperatures. They begin to disperse in their 5th instar, and in their 6th and final instar become solitary. Then they pupate in low grass or tussocks and leaf litter. The peak flight period is the end of May to mid-June. By mid-July they are gone.

Marsh Fritillaries undergo great fluctuations in numbers, with periodic crashes and expansions. The years 1982-1985 were a time of expansion, followed by more lean years in core sites. The reverses are connected to variations in food supply, weather and parasitism of the caterpillars by braconid wasps of the genus *Cotesia*. There is considerable movement of populations of this butterfly, with patterns of dispersal, new colonization and local extinctions characteristic of metapopulations. The Action Plan for *E. aurinia* reports that although there are 35 definite sites in Scotland, "the situation is not as healthy as might be assumed from these figures as most colonies are small and their extinction rate is high (Barnett and Warren 1995b, 10)." Clearly this is a seriously endangered butterfly, and has the highest level of legal protection. An important initiative in September 2001 brought together farmers, landowners and conservationists on Islay to discuss the needs of farmers and the butterfly. The farmers are crucial to the survival of this Fritillary, dependent as it is on low-intensity cattle- and sheep-grazing pastures.

The **Wall** (*Lasiommata megera*) is limited in its Scottish range, quite like the Large Skipper, to the coastal areas of Ayrshire, Dumfries and Galloway. There has been a sprinkling of sightings further up the west and east coasts. It has been spotted at St. Abb's Head, and I myself saw one flattened against a wire mesh fence on the cliffs above St. Andrews Bay in May 1993, clearly a detained voyager on a blustery southern wind. Its distribution in England is narrowing in the south, and moving northwards, but there is little evidence that it is making much headway beyond its southwestern strongholds within Scotland.

The **Mountain Ringlet** (*Erebia epiphron scotica*) was one of the first butterflies, along with *Aricia artaxerxes* and possibly *Erebia aethiops*, to colonize in the Late Glacial period. It is now confined to two of the areas occupied at that time, the Scottish Highlands and the Lake District, and is the only montane butterfly in the UK. A recent report has cast doubt on its ability to survive beyond the year 2050 if present levels of increases in climate warming continue. Studies at Ben Lawers NNR suggest a 1°C or 2°C rise in mean temperatures would reduce suitable habitat by 40 %, but its adaptability may be being underestimated. It has, after all, millennia of experience in Scotland! The survey for the 2001 *Atlas* failed to re-record *E. epiphron scotica* in 12 10 km squares where it was found in 1970-1982, but discovered the butterfly in 22 new 10 km squares. This is an increase of 34 %. Weather conditions are, of course, a major factor in the flight of this Ringlet, and I recorded excellent numbers in the mountains above Kinloch Rannoch in 2000, followed by none at all in 2001. There is almost certainly a two-year cycle allowing it to circumvent poor seasons, and maybe there is even a three-year seasonal cycle.

The flight period is relatively short occurring any weather-suitable time between June and early August in Scotland. It lasts some 2-4 weeks, and the peak is quickly reached after emergence. Adults can fly in overcast and rainy conditions so long as the temperature is 13-14°C. Its primary foodplant is probably mat-grass (*Nardus stricta*) along with sheep's-fescue (*Festuca ovina*), and that 'probably' indicates the difficulty of studying the ecology of this butterfly, as anyone who has tried to monitor eggs and larvae can testify. Indeed one Report has surmised that "caterpillars may be more abundant at nights" (Pearce et al 1999, 9). The larvae feed at night, dropping to the base of tussocks by day. They hibernate in late August or September and emerge in spring. The imago takes nectar from whatever flowers are available.

The Scottish Mountain Ringlet is larger and often has brighter colouration than the Lake District species (*E.e piphron mnemon*). Colonies occur between 350-900 m and occasionally over 1000 m, but most are found between 450-800 m (Thomson 1980, 173). They are usually south-facing in Scotland, while those in the Lake District have various aspects that include northerly. Populations shift slightly from year to year, and depend upon some sheep grazing to keep the turf at a required height. Adults fly close to the ground with males more active moving as far as 200 m per flight. The putative foodplant, mat-grass, is abundant on 99 % of mountains in the UK.

There are some other rare butterflies to be seen in Scotland, but most are not established here.

The **Camberwell Beauty** (*Nymphalis antiopa*) was recorded in Sutherland and Shetland in 1995, and sporadically in 1996 as a result of a strong airflow in high-pressure conditions coming from Scandinavia. **Clouded Yellow** (*Colias croceus*) is quite a regular visitor to Scotland with occasional invasions of large numbers as in 1992 when they swept through the Central Belt. And there were considerable numbers in 2000. *The Millennium Atlas* foresees the possibility of this species establishing permanent populations as a result of global warming (Asher et al 2001, 95). **The Holly Blue** (*Celastrina argiolus*) is a desultory visitor seen occasionally at Rockcliffe in the southwest, and one in the East Neuk in 1998. **The Brimstone** (*Gonepteryx rhamni*) is a very rare sight in Scotland, though I have seen one outside Dunning, which was almost certainly a home-bred release. The prolific Buckthorn running from Kinshaldy towards St. Andrews could, perhaps, be seriously considered for the introduction of this butterfly by SNH. True, the buckthorn is north-facing, but the Brimstone is a resourceful butterfly which can fly 11 months of the year. And finally there is the **Comma** (*Polygonia c-album*), perhaps a resident insect already. Over the past 5 years, it has expanded into the Borders and Lothian, and with its northerly migration, promises to establish itself firmly over this decade. The outlook for countryside species like *c-album* within Scotland is clearer than for the habitat-specialist species. The progress of the **Orange-tip** (*Anthocharis cardamines*) may be a prelude to the progress of the more adaptable countryside butterflies. It has increased in Scotland by 100 % over the past 30 years.

So what of the future for Scotland's butterflies? With regard to the Central Belt, the future is not promising. The increase in building, the wish to tidy up anything that looks a little unruly – all these patterns of 'progress' are inimitable to butterflies. Peacocks, Red Admirals and Small Tortoiseshells like nothing better than a good clump of stinging nettles. A further impending problem could arise as a result of demise of the Longannet Deep Mine. Some reasonable compromise solutions have led to a slow down by opencast companies but the fear must be that there will be a new push to exploit surface coal whatever the ecological consequences.

The rarer butterflies of Scotland have long been in retreat from the Central Belt. Where until very recently Glen Ledknock hosted the last of the habitat species near the Belt, the Pearl-bordered Fritillary has now retreated to Loch

Tay. In regard to global warming, the long-term effects are not as clear as the short-term. For now, warming has led to a shift northwards in some butterfly ranges but the release of billions of gallons of icy water from melting glaciers, with its impact on the Gulf Stream, could reverse this warming over a period of time, and maybe plunge the Scottish climate into a much colder phase. One of the most sensitive barometers of these changes is insect life, since it is integral to changes happening on the earth's surface. This provides an urgent reason for us all to study what is going on in the natural world of Scotland's lepidoptera.

References and further reading

Asher, Jim et al (2001). *The Millennium Atlas of Butterflies in Britain and Ireland.* Oxford University Press.

Barnett, L.K. and Warren, M.S. (1995a). *Marsh Fritillary Species Action Plan.* Butterfly Conservation, Wareham.

Barnett, L.K. and Warren, M.S. (1995b). *Pearl-bordered Fritillary Species Action Plan.* Butterfly Conservation, Wareham.

Bayfield, N. et al (1995). Small Mountain Ringlet project: field studies, rearing programme and questionnaire survey 1994-1995. Institute of Terrestrial Ecology.

Bourn, N.A.D., Jeffcoate, G.E. and Warren, M.S. (2000). *Dingy Skipper Species Action Plan.* Butterfly Conservation , Wareham.

Bourn, N.A.D. and Warren, M.S. (2000). *Small Blue Species Action Plan.* Butterfly Conservation, Wareham.

Bowles, Nick (2001). Wildlife Reports: 'Butterflies.' *British Wildlife*, 13:2, December 2001.

Bowles, Nick (2002). Wildlife Reports: 'Butterflies.' *British Wildlife*, 13:3, February 2002.

Boyd, Brian and Pyle, Robert Michael (2000). *Nabokov's Butterflies: unpublished and uncollected writings.* Allen Lane, London.

Butterfly Conservation News, 1997-2002.

Brown, Lesley (2000). *Butterflies of the Forth Valley.* CARSE, Stirling.

Clunas, A. (1986). The biology and habitat requirements of *Aricia artaxerxes* Fabricius (Lep: Lycaenidae). Thesis, University of Edinburgh.

Dennis, R.L.H. (1977). *The British Butterflies.* Classey, Oxford.

Emmet, A.M. and Heath, J. (1989). *The Moths and Butterflies of Great Britain and Ireland.* 7 part 1 *Hesperiidae to Nymphalidae.* Hartley Books, Colchester.

Fox, R. et al (2001). *The State of Britain's Butterflies.* Butterfly Conservation, CEH & JNCC, Wareham.

Hancock, E.G. (1998). Insect Records for 1996. *Glasgow Naturalist*, 23: part 3, 27-30.

Hancock, E.G. (1999). Insect Records for 1997. *Glasgow Naturalist*, 23: part 4, 55-58.

Hancock, E.G. (2000). Insect Records for 1998 and 1999. *Glasgow Naturalist*, 23: part 5, 48-52.

Hancock, E.G. (2001). Insect Records for 2000. *Glasgow Naturalist*, 23: part 6, 53-56.

Heath, J., Pollard, E. and Thomas, J.A. (1984). *Atlas of Butterflies in Britain and Ireland.* Viking, London.

Higgins, L.G. and Riley, N.D. (1970). *A Field Guide to the Butterflies of Britain and Europe.* Collins, London.

O'Keefe, J. (1995). Habitat Management of Marsh Fritillaries (Eurodryas aurinia). M.Sc. Thesis, University of Edinburgh.

Pearce, I.S.K. et al (1999). *Scottish diurnal lepidopteral project; sites, protocols, and distribution* (SNH research, survey and monitoring report, no. 113).

Pollard, E. and Yates, T.J. (1993). *Monitoring Butterflies for Ecology and Conservation.* Chapman & Hall, London.

Ravenscroft, N.O.M. (1996). *The Chequered Skipper.* Butterfly Conservation, Dedham.

Ravenscroft, N.O.M. and Warren, M.S. (1996a). *Chequered Skipper Species Action Plan.* Butterfly Conservation, Wareham.

Ravenscroft, N.O.M. and Warren, M.S. (1996b). *Mountain Ringlet Species Action Plan.* Butterfly Conservation, Wareham.

Ravenscroft, N.O.M. and Warren, M.S. (1995). *Northern Brown Argus Species Action Plan; Second Draft.* Butterfly Conservation, Wareham.

Ravenscroft, N.O.M. and Warren, M.S. (1996c). *Northern Brown Argus Species Action Plan.* Butterfly Conservation, Wareham.

Ravenscroft, N.O.M. and Gaywood, M.J. (1996). *The status and habitat of the marsh fritillary butterfly in western Scotland* (SNH research, survey and monitoring report, no. 21).

Ravenscroft, N.O.M. (1994a). The Ecology of the Chequered Skipper Butterfly *Carterocephalus palaemon* in Scotland. 1. Microhabitat. *Journal of Applied Ecology,* 31: 613-622.

Ravenscroft, N.O.M. (1994b). The Ecology of the Chequered Skipper Butterfly *Carterocephalus palaemon* in Scotland. 2. Foodplant quality and population range. *Journal of Applied Ecology,* 31: 623-630.

Ravenscroft, N.O.M. (1994c). The Feeding Behaviour of *Carterocephalus palaemon* (Lepidoptera: Hesperiidae) Caterpillars: does it avoid host defences or maximize nutrient intake? *Ecological Entomology,* 19: 26-30.

Spooner, D. (1997). The Chequered Skipper and Butterfly Conservation in Scotland. *Forth Naturalist and Historian,* 20: 57-60.

Thomson, G. (1980). *The Butterflies of Scotland.* Croom Helm, London.

Thomson, G. (1976). Our 'Disappearing' Butterflies. *Forth Naturalist and Historian,* 1: 89-105.

Thomson, G. (1977). Migrant Butterflies of Central Scotland. *Forth Naturalist and Historian,* 2: 49-53.

Warren, M.S. (1991). *The Chequered Skipper, Carterocephalus palaemon in Northern Europe.* Butterfly Conservation, Wareham.

Warren, M.S. (1992). Britain's Vanishing Fritillaries. *British Wildlife,* 3: 282-296.

Warren, M.S., Clarke, S. and Currie, F. (2001). The Coppice for Butterflies Challenge: a targeted grant scheme for threatened species. *British Wildlife,* 13: 21-28.

Warren, M.S. et al (2001). Rapid responses of British butterflies to opposing forces of climate and habitat change. *Nature,* 414: 6859, 67-70.

Warren, M.S. (1994). The UK status and suspected metapopulation structure of a threatened European butterfly, the marsh fritillary *Eurodryas aurinia. Biological Conservation,* 67: 239-249.

Wheeler, A.S. (1982). *Erebia epiphron* Knoch (Lep., Satyridae) reared on a two-year life cycle. *Proceedings of the British Entomological and Natural History Society,* 15: 28.

Willcox, Neil (1999). Butterfly Havens. *Scottish Wildlife,* 37: 16-18.

Glossary

biodiversity The variety of life on the planet, or any given part of it. There is no finer account than that found in Edward O. Wilson, *The Diversity of Life* (Harvard University Press paperback, 1992).

colony A group of individual butterflies occurring in a distinct habitat apparently separated from other groups of the same species.

coppicing A traditional method of management of broad-leaved trees, producing a supply of poles by cutting just above the base of the trunk on a regular, usually 7-year, cycle. This allows the trees to regenerate, but allows more glades with sunlight for lepidoptera.

flight period The length of the adult (flying) period.

foodplant The plant species on which the butterfly caterpillars feed.

hibernaculum The shelter of an overwintering larva, usually created from a leaf.

imago The final, fully developed adult stage of insect development, following the larval and pupal stages.

instar A stage of growth between successive moults in caterpillars.

introduction The intentional or accidental release of an organism to a place outside its recent range.

reintroduction The intentional release of an organism into a part of its native range from which it has become extinct.

Species Action Plans Plans that began in the 1990s, drawn up by Butterfly Conservation in response to the (continuing) serious problems for butterflies with special habitat needs.

univoltine Having one brood or generation each year.

A personal reminiscence of Dr. John Berry (1907-2002)

John Berry's contribution to conservation and knowledge of biodiversity in Scotland is little short of phenomenal. He could have had no finer tutor in these matters than a regular visitor to his childhood home at Tayfield, Patrick Geddes – whose magnificent plans for a Nature Palace down the road at Dunfermline had been deemed too visionary in 1904. I will not try to list all Dr. Berry's achievements, but to mention a few – he was fish scientist to the new Hydro Board, and conceived the fish ladder at the dam at Pitlochry; he was a founder of the International Union for the Preservation of Nature at Fontainebleau in 1948 and the first director of Nature Conservancy in Scotland in 1949. He was a member of the International Committee for Bird Preservation, and wrote the definitive *The status and distribution of wild geese and wild duck in Scotland* in 1939. To him we owe a whole range of Scottish nature reserves from the Cairngorms to Tentsmuir on his doorstep. A full list of his public offices can be seen in the latest *Who's Who*.

But I should like to add some memories of his interest in lepidoptera. I recall a visit where there was great excitement while he gathered in for examination a stray Mouse Moth. He had rigged up what he called the Tayfield Insect House next to the Garden House he and his wife, Bride, lived in. With typical ingenuity, he had adapted an old boiler to fuel it as a home to a myriad of moths. I have in front of me a photograph of one moth of which he was especially proud. It was an Indian Moon Moth (*Actias selene*) which normally has two tail strands, but which in this case had a stunted, defective left tail. The Edinburgh Butterfly House supplied him with his larvae, and one of the clues to his amazing youthfulness even in his 80s and 90s was his love of lepidoptera. Their flights and distinctive characters – for contrary to appearances, individual butterflies and moths do respond differently – appealed to something in his nature. I only knew him in the last decade of his life, but I recall that when we had chatted, he remarked "so you are another crazy mixed-up kid just like me!" Well, with an introduction like that one knew that for all his honours, there was no way John Berry stood on formality. Although he had suffered from the bone-wasting Paget's Disease for some 30 years, this never hindered his getting about his lepidopteral investigations.

There was further lepidopteral excitement when he discovered a dwarf Small White (*Pieris rapae*) in his garden, which he got me to send to the Natural History Museum at Kensington. As it happened, that Museum had a number of examples already, but I have not heard of many such specimens within Scotland. I still have the creature in all its fragile glory. It serves to recall a man of truly natural modesty, who yet entertained a herculean determination to secure Scotland's natural heritage for future generations. Patrick Geddes remarked (in his Report on Dunfermline in 1904) that "the east coast of Scotland has furnished many and marked examples of men of naturalist genius who have broken through all the difficulties of their circumstances to an original grasp of things." Dr. John Berry deserves pride of place in the Scottish Hall of Ecological fame alongside such as David Douglas, George Forrest, Robert Fortune, Joseph Dalton Hooker (who grew up in Glasgow), D'Arcy Wentworth Thompson and Geddes himself.

Books referred to:

John Berry, *The status and distribution of wild geese and wild duck in Scotland*. Cambridge University Press, 1939.

Patrick Geddes, *City development, a study of parks, gardens, and culture-institutes; a report to the Carnegie Dunfermline Trust*. Edinburgh 1904; reprinted by the Irish University Press, Dublin, 1973.

FRESHWATER FISH OF THE LOCH LOMOND AND THE TROSSACHS NATIONAL PARK

Peter S. Maitland

Although there are still many gaps, a wide variety of information is available regarding the fresh waters and fish of the Loch Lomond and the Trossachs National Park. Altogether there are hundreds of relevant publications and reports and these have recently been drawn together in a bibliography of published work concerning the area involved (Maitland 2001). For example, in considering Loch Lomond alone there are well over 100 references. Some of the publications are merely short notes on a particular aquatic plant or animal species (e.g. Kerr and Mitchell, 1981) or a particular water body (e.g. Lee, 1951). Others are much more important, and may be a long-term or extensive study of one water (e.g. Slack, 1965) or a broader based survey of several waters (e.g. Smith *et al.* 1987).

The final boundary of the National Park is now established (Figure 1). In places this does follow watersheds and administrative boundaries, but elsewhere its course is rather arbitrary cutting across catchments to include, in places, the headwaters of some river systems, elsewhere, the lower reaches of others. Though there are few problems in considering individual standing waters within the area the unusual nature of the boundary does raise difficulties in relation to running waters and overall management strategies.

FRESH WATERS OF THE AREA

The Loch Lomond and the Trossachs National Park contains a very wide variety of fresh waters from the smallest trickles and pools to the largest area of fresh water in Great Britain (Figure 1). There is a wide range in altitude from sea level to 1,000 m and in chemistry from extremely nutrient poor (oligotrophic) to very nutrient rich (eutrophic). Most of the water bodies are natural and unpolluted but there are artificial waters and some polluted waters also. Part of the interesting natural variation in the area is due to the Highland Boundary Fault which crosses through from southwest to northeast, with generally upland nutrient poor ground to the north and lowland nutrient rich ground to the south. The area is relatively sparsely populated and there is little industry. The main occupations are related to farming, forestry and tourism. Water based recreation of all kinds is very popular.

Standing waters: lochs and ponds

The standing waters of the area range from the numerous small pools and lochans (especially common in the uplands) to Loch Lomond, which is the largest area of fresh water in Great Britain, with a surface area of 71 km^2. The largest lochs (those over 1 km^2) are all of significance forming an extremely important resource. Some of them are extremely important for several reasons and are examples of multi-purpose usage. In some places these uses are compatible, in others they are not.

Medium-sized lochs may also be important and again some have multi-purpose usage. Several are entirely natural (e.g. Loch Restil, Geal Loch) whereas others are actually artificial reservoirs (e.g. Muir Park Reservoir). Virtually all of them are used for angling and as the demands for this sport increase so are more and more smaller and smaller waters brought into use (or even created) for this purpose – many of them as put-and-take fisheries.

The smallest lochs and pools are of less direct use to humans but can be extremely valuable for wildlife and are an important conservation feature of the area. The upland waters in this category tend to be natural but in the lowlands many are artificial (i.e. small reservoirs, curling ponds, old gravel pits, etc.). A review of those occurring in the former Central Region (ca. 300 waters) was carried out as part of the Scottish Conservation Projects Operation Brightwater project (Lassiere, 1993).

Running waters: rivers and streams

Five major river systems are represented in the area – Eachaig, Earn, Forth, Leven and Tay. The latter is the largest river by flow in Great Britain, but only its head waters occur within the National Park (Maitland and Smith, 1987). The medium-sized rivers are all tributaries of the above, but many are of importance in their own right (e.g. the River Endrick). Most are accessible to migratory fish and important as spawning and nursery grounds.

The smallest rivers are extremely numerous, especially in the upland areas, and mostly drain to the larger systems mentioned above. A number are inaccessible to migratory fish. Many, however, drain directly into the larger lochs in the study area (e.g. Loch Lomond, Loch Earn) and may be of importance in their own right as spawning and nursery areas for specific substocks of Salmon or Trout, or for other reasons.

THE FISH FAUNA OF THE AREA

The list of freshwater fish which occur in the area includes 37 of the Scottish total of 42 (Table 1). Several of them are introductions to Great Britain from abroad: Rainbow Trout, Brook Charr, Common Carp, Crucian Carp, Goldfish, Orfe, or to Scotland from England: Common Bream, Gudgeon, Chub, Dace, Rudd, Tench, Ruffe, Grayling – and are not therefore of especial conservation concern (Maitland and Lyle, 1991). Other fish are essentially marine or estuarine species e.g. Sea Bass, Thick-lipped and Thin-lipped Mullet, Common Goby, or marine vagrants to the area e.g. Sturgeon and Allis and Twaite Shad – and are of less direct relevance to the area, which includes little marine habitat.

Native species of especial note in the area are River Lamprey, Sea Lamprey, Powan and Arctic Charr.

The River Lamprey is relatively common in Great Britain south of the Great Glen. It is normally migratory with a larval freshwater phase in rivers and an adult parasitic phase in estuaries. In the Loch Lomond catchment, uniquely in Britain, it is entirely a freshwater species – the adults feeding on Powan in Loch Lomond instead of migrating to salt water (Maitland, 1980). In addition, the Loch Lomond race is very different morphologically from the normal form. Thus this population merits especial attention and appropriate conservation measures.

The Sea Lamprey is found in several running waters, notably the Rivers Leven, Teith and Forth. The Leven population is of particular interest as it appears that some of the juvenile population (which normally descend to the sea to feed on marine fish) stays on in fresh water in Loch Lomond where it parasitises Salmon and Sea Trout.

The Powan is one of our rarest fish and occurs in only two waters – Loch Lomond and Loch Eck – both within the National Park. Although Loch Lomond is large, Powan there are under pressure from various uses of the loch and from fish introductions. To ensure the survival of this stock, fish for translocation have been collected in several years when Powan spawn in January by stripping adults of eggs and milt. Eggs are hatched indoors and young released at two sites – Loch Sloy and Carron Reservoir. Both of these new populations appear to be doing well.

The Arctic Charr is also under threat in various parts of the British Isles and has disappeared from a number of lochs in Scotland (e.g. Loch Grannoch, Loch Leven, St. Mary's Loch). Several populations occur in the area and have been separated from others for many thousands of years. The population in Loch Eck is an unusual deep water form, but those in the Trossachs lochs are also of considerable scientific importance.

Other species of note in the area are Brook Lamprey (which, like the other lampreys, is listed in Annex II of the EU Habitats Directive) and Nine-spined Stickleback. The latter is becoming quite rare in Scotland and, though there is a population in Loch Lomond, virtually nothing is know about its habits there.

FRESHWATER FISHERIES

Salmon

The area includes parts of the catchments of several important salmon waters, including the Rivers Tay, Earn (with Loch Earn), Teith (with Lochs Voil, Doine and Lubnaig), Forth (with Loch Ard), Leven (with Loch Lomond) and Eachaig (with Loch Eck). Most of these waters are important, either directly for salmon angling or indirectly as spawning and nursery habitat for young fish.

Catches of Atlantic Salmon by Fishery District are reported annually by the Scottish Executive. Although the National Park boundary does not encompass all the Fishery Districts concerned, the bulk of the fish caught in the Clyde, Eachaig and, to a lesser extent, the Forth systems are taken within its boundary.

As in the rest of Scotland, the Atlantic Salmon is an important species in economic terms in the Loch Lomond and the Trossachs area and contributes substantially to local recreation and employment. Precise figures are not available for the whole of the National Park but Mackay Consultants 1989 estimated that in the Loch Lomond area alone there were 11,100 angler days in 1988 and that the average daily expenditure for all anglers was £21.11. The total expenditure generated by anglers in the Loch Lomond area in 1988 was estimated at £236,491. Thus for the whole Loch Lomond and Trossachs area the annual expenditure related to salmon and sea trout fishing is likely to be several times this figure.

Trout

Trout are probably the commonest fish over the area as a whole and both Brown Trout and Sea Trout are found. The latter is largely restricted to running waters and associated large lochs with reasonable access from the sea but Brown Trout are common in the great majority of lochs, rivers and streams. Thousands of anglers fish for trout in the area and, though no figures are available, the species is undoubtedly of considerable importance to the local economy.

Rainbow Trout, originally introduced from North America, is a popular sport species in some waters. Though it has never managed to establish itself in the area, it is bred in large numbers on fish farms and introduced to various waters (e.g. the Loch of Menteith), sometimes as young fish but more often on a put-and-take basis. This is also the species most commonly farmed for the table.

Other species

Arctic Charr are caught inadvertently by some game anglers but are the specific target of a few specialists. This fish is likely to become more popular in future years.

Coarse fishing is increasingly popular with anglers, and people in England (and even elsewhere in Europe, e.g. the Netherlands) are becoming aware of the excellent coarse fishing available in the area. The main species angled for are Pike, Perch, Roach and Eels, and Loch Lomond is becoming particularly well known for large specimen fish of all these species (Maitland, 1990).

From time to time Eels have been fished commercially from several waters in the area (e.g. Loch Lomond), using fyke nets, but such fisheries have not proved sustainable and populations have dropped quickly below commercially viable numbers.

During the two World Wars, Powan was fished commercially in both Loch Lomond and Loch Eck and several hundred thousand fish were taken as a valued food during this period.

CURRENT THREATS

Only in recent years has society become aware of the enormous damage being done to natural resources. Human influence on fresh waters is no exception. The conflict between the demand for large amounts of pure water on the one hand, and the disastrous pollution of many waters on the other, is only now forcing the issue in many parts of the world. Multi-purpose river-basin projects and comprehensive catchment management are the logical solution to many problems. In general terms, the area is fortunate in having few major threats to its fresh waters. There are a number of problems, however, and the following brief accounts indicate the major impacts of human usage on the ecology of freshwater systems in the area.

Pollution

Domestic and industrial discharges can act in three main ways: by settling out on the substratum and smothering life there, by being acutely toxic and killing organisms directly, or by reducing the oxygen supply so much as to kill organisms indirectly. Effluents with high suspended solids are typical of mining industries, poorly treated domestic sewage, and various washing processes. Several instances of this type of pollution have occurred in the area in the past, including washings from sand and gravel works which have polluted the River Fruin (CRPB 1988), severe wash off from road construction, again into the River Fruin and Loch Lomond (CRPB 1986, 1990) and erosion from poor forestry practice (CRPB 1986). If the particles involved are organic, their decay may add the problem of deoxygenation to that of alteration of the substratum.

The impact of toxic substances on organisms in natural waters is complicated by the fact that different species have varying resistance thresholds to poisons. Although there is relatively little industry in the area, fresh waters have been subject to toxic events for example from sheep dipping and the effluent from silage; examples are at the Catter Burn (CRPB 1986), Tarr Burn (FRPB 1989, 1990) and a fish kill in the Mar Burn due to silage liquor discharge (CRPB 1986). Organic materials in sewage effluents are a source of major pollution of fresh waters. Mild organic pollution is found in many streams just below sewage works serving the many communities in the area. Occasionally, through overloading or faults at the sewage works, serious pollution has developed, for example from the Duck Bay Marina to Loch Lomond (CRPB 1988) and the Leisure Centre at Lochgoilhead into the River Goil (CRPB 1988).

Eutrophication occurs when the nutrient salts present increase and problems of algal blooms, deoxygenation and fish kills develop – especially in lochs. There is clear evidence that many waters in the study area are suffering from eutrophication, and problems are believed to exist at Loch Lomond (CRPB 1986), Loch Earn (TRPB 1990) and the Trossachs lochs (FRPB 1990).

Acidification has resulted in severe damage to fish in parts of the National Park; some hill lochs on granite (e.g. lochans west of Maol Meadhonach) are now fishless (Maitland *et al.*, 1987. The Loch Lomond Angling Improvement's fish hatchery was forced to introduce calcium to its water supply to prevent fish deaths (LLAIA 1986) in some locations. Extensive studies of water chemistry, invertebrates and fish in the Loch Ard area have shown that fish are absent from many streams because of high acidity (Harriman and Morrison 1981, 1982; SOAFD 1990), though the situation now seems to be improving.

Land use

There has been little canalisation of the major rivers in the area, but many minor streams have been straightened and ditched by agriculture and forestry practices. In addition there has been extensive land drainage in relation to both farming and forestry. The past clearing of forests has increased the run-off of surface water and the rate of soil erosion with subsequent silting and nutrient increase in the waters draining such areas (Maitland *et al.*, 1990). Several of these problems have occurred in the area. In one case, bad drainage practice led to severe local erosion and subsequent silting in the River Fruin (CRPB 1990). The purification board considered that the river was so severely polluted by surface runoff that they considered prosecution. However, the company concerned carried out major drainage alterations which improved water quality. In the Loch Ard area it has been shown that, in areas of poor soil, streams running through the forest are acidified and fishless whilst those on adjacent moorland have healthy populations (Harriman and Morrison 1981, 1982, SOAFD 1990). Most types of cultivation lead to loss of soil and nutrients; deficiency of the latter is commonly overcome by the regular addition of agricultural fertilisers. These too tend to be washed off and affect the nutrient status and ecology of waters into which they drain. Rapid eutrophication caused by increased nutrient input from fertilisers and sewage effluents is one of the major problems in the management of fresh waters today (Maitland, 1984) and, as noted above, is a common feature in lochs in the lowland parts of the area (e.g. Loch Earn).

Water use

Substantial quantities of water are piped from Loch Lomond and so much less water flows down the River Leven. The long-established water supply scheme involving Loch Katrine and adjacent lochs pipes water south to Glasgow and thus reduces flow in the Rivers Teith and Forth. There are many minor schemes, some of which do have local effects. There are numerous reservoirs in the area some of them quite large (e.g. Glen Finglas Reservoir). In addition, several large lochs (e.g. Lochs Lomond, Katrine, Venacher) have been impounded by small dams or barrages so that their water level is now controlled artificially.

The major hydro-electric schemes in the study area are at Loch Sloy (where a small natural loch was impounded and flooded to create a large reservoir), at Loch na Lairige (where a new reservoir was created) and at Loch Earn. There is little evidence that these relatively small schemes have had much ecological impact other than substantial loss of water in the lower reaches of the original streams flooded.

Fish farms pose a number of environmental problems, notably concerning pollution, disease and fish escapes. Fish farms in the area include those on the Glenry and Malling Burns (FRPB 1990) and the fish cage farm in Loch Earn (TRPB 1989). Some years ago a proposal to install fish cages on Loch Lomond was turned down on the grounds of likely environmental damage.

Recreation

There has been increasing controversy in recent years concerning the impact of angling on aquatic wildlife. A central problem concerns litter, which, in addition to being unsightly has a serious impact on birds and mammals because of hooks and monofilament line in which they become entangled. The presence of anglers often disturbs wildlife. Anglers can alter habitat, either unintentionally (e.g. by trampling down vegetation), or intentionally (e.g. weed cutting and bank clearance). Anglers may also impinge directly on aquatic communities by poisoning unwanted fish, shooting predatory birds or introducing new fish species. Stocking with desired fish species to enhance the population may have the opposite effect. The reasons for this are varied but include the introduction of disease, overstocking and the elimination of important genetic components evolved by the native stock.

Several of these problems have arisen in the area. For example, at Loch Lomond where it is known that the fish community has been stable for hundreds of years with 14 native species (Maitland, 1972), coarse fishermen have introduced several species new to the area in recent years and four of these (Gudgeon, Chub, Dace and Ruffe) have become well established in the last decade (Maitland and East, 1989). The Ruffe is particularly unwelcome, for it was previously unknown in Scotland (Maitland *et al.*, 1983), but is now one of the commonest fish in Loch Lomond (and in the Rivers Endrick and Leven), where it it known to feed extensively on the eggs of Powan and to have affected other aspects of local ecology (Adams and Maitland, 1998).

Elsewhere, the native fish populations of some waters (e.g. Loch Ruskie) have been eliminated by poison to make way for stocked trout fisheries.

In contrast to nature conservation and water pollution control management, the management of fish stocks and fisheries in the area (as in much of the rest of Scotland) has, until recently, been piecemeal, often misguided (and even harmful to stocks) and completely lacking in any integrated policy related to sustainability. Thus dozens of individual management practices are carried out on different waters (sometimes even on different parts of the same water) throughout the area. Often fishery management policy changes completely with the owner of the water. Since there is no national plan or policy and, in part, inadequate legislation, a wide variety of, mostly unscientific, management practices have taken place over recent decades. These have mostly been completely legal but have involved the following: the complete elimination of native fish stocks using piscicides, the blanket removal of supposed predators (e.g. Pike) using gill nets and other means, the application of lime and occasionally fertilisers to 'improve' water quality, the regular introduction of non-native stocks of salmonids (including

Salmon, Brown Trout and Sea Trout – some of foreign origin), the development of put-and-take fisheries (mainly for Brown and Rainbow Trout) where farmed fish are released at catchable size to be caught at any time thereafter (sometimes the day after release), the transfer of coarse fish (sometimes being used as livebait) from one water (sometimes one country) to another, the wholesale removal of riparian vegetation of importance to wildlife.

DISCUSSION

Four of the larger waters of the area stand out as being of enormous importance, locally, nationally and internationally – Loch Lomond, Loch Eck, the River Endrick and the River Teith. High priority must be given to their conservation needs which are not yet being sufficiently respected.

Loch Lomond is unquestionably of major significance in a wide variety of contexts, locally, nationally and internationally (Maitland, 1972, 1983). As with Loch Eck, it is essential that if this unique freshwater body is to be managed for the future and in a sustainable way, then a conservation management programme for land use and activities in the catchment of the loch (at present in preparation) must be instigated as well as an appropriate management policy for the loch itself.

Loch Eck is of outstanding significance because of its fish community which is unique in the British Isles and of international significance. The Powan is found in only one other loch in Scotland (Loch Lomond) and in only five other sites elsewhere in the British Isles. In one of these sites (Haweswater in Cumbria), Powan and Arctic Charr occur together - as they do at Loch Eck and these are the only two waters in the British Isles where this combination occurs. However, whilst Haweswater is now substantially degraded, because it is used extensively for water supply, Loch Eck is still very largely natural and indeed a good example of a classical highland oligotrophic loch. In addition to Powan and Arctic Charr, Atlantic Salmon and Sea Trout occur in Loch Eck. No other water in the British Isles has this combination of species and indeed, outside Scandinavia and western Russia this fish community is unique in Europe.

The River Endrick is notable not only as the major spawning and nursery area for Atlantic Salmon and Brown Trout in the Loch Lomond catchment, but also for its populations of River and Brook Lampreys, the former being a form unique in the British Isles. Parts of the River Endrick are now a Special Area of Conservation (SAC) for these species. In addition, the Endrick catchment includes seven SSSIs (some with freshwater interest), part of a local Country Park (Mugdock), an SWT Nature Reserve (Loch Ardinning) and the only known Scottish site (the Altquhur Burn) for the rare subterranean crustacean *Bathynella natans* (Maitland, 1962). The omission of most of the River Endrick and its catchment from the Loch Lomond and the Trossachs National Park was a curious decision and one with which the author has always disagreed.

The River Teith system from its source to its confluence with the River Forth runs across varying geology, from nutrient poor erosion resistant metamorphic rocks above 500 m in altitude, to richer Old Red Sandstone at lower altitudes. The diversity of geological features and aquatic environments result in an exceptionally wide variety of habitats within the freshwater system. This system supports an outstanding range of freshwater, and notably riverine, plant and animal communities in natural succession. The range of community succession is probably unparalleled in any other British river and several of the communities represent the most species-rich examples of their type yet found. Because of its populations of lampreys (River, Brook and Sea Lampreys are found here) the Teith, like the Endrick, has also been declared a Special Area of Conservation. The Teith system includes Loch Doine, Loch Voil and Loch Lubnaig which form a series of nutrient poor to moderately nutrient rich waters. All have populations of Arctic Charr.

CONCLUSIONS

The main conclusions drawn from this review of the fish fauna of the Loch Lomond and the Trossachs National Park are as follows:

The area is rich in fresh waters, small and large, of a wide variety of types. Waters of international, national and local conservation importance occur there; in particular, Loch Lomond, Loch Eck, the River Endrick and the River Teith are of outstanding significance. There are also several Sites of Special Scientific Interest in the area which are of importance for their fresh waters. Some of these are of international status.

Thirty-seven freshwater fish species occur in the area – 23 (62 %) of these are native to the area and 14 (38 %) are alien. The species of greatest conservation importance are Sea Lamprey, River Lamprey, Powan and Arctic Charr. The fresh waters of the area are the basis of several major fisheries (for Salmon, Brown and Sea Trout and Rainbow Trout) which are of economic importance to the surrounding communities.

The area is quite sparsely populated but there are significant threats to its fresh waters from industrial and domestic effluents, industrial developments (including roads), acid deposition, land use (farming and forestry), drainage works, water abstraction, recreation and angling and fishery management. Management policies could be improved in relation to nature conservation, are unsound for some forms of land and water use and are completely inadequate for fisheries and fish stocks. The major issue in relation to the future conservation of fresh waters and fish in the area lies in developing sound catchment-based land-use and water-use management policies.

REFERENCES

Adams, C.E. and Maitland, P.S. 1998. The Ruffe population of Loch Lomond, Scotland: Its introduction, population expansion, and interaction with native species. *International Association for Great Lakes Research* 24, 249-262

CRPB. 1986. *Annual Report.* East Kilbride, Clyde River Purification Board.

CRPB. 1988. *Annual Report.* East Kilbride, Clyde River Purification Board.

CRPB. 1990. *Annual Report.* East Kilbride, Clyde River Purification Board.
FRPB. 1989. *Annual Report.* Edinburgh, Forth River Purification Board.
FRPB. 1990. *Annual Report.* Edinburgh, Forth River Purification Board.
Harriman, R. and Morrison, B.R.S. 1981. Forestry, acid rain and fisheries in Scotland. *Scottish Forestry.* 35, 89-95.
Harriman, R. and Morrison, B.R.S. 1982. Ecology of streams draining forested and non-forested catchments in an area of central Scotland subject to acid precipitation. *Hydrobiologia* 88, 252-263.
Kerr, A.J. and Mitchell, J. 1981. Water Shrew *Neomys fodiens* at Rossdhu, Loch Lomondside. *Glasgow Naturalist* 20, 183-184.
Lassiere, O.L. 1993. *Central Region Lochs and Ponds.* Stirling, Scottish Conservation Projects.
Lee, J.R. 1951. A visit to the source of the River Falloch. *Glasgow Naturalist* 7, 65-77.
LLAIA. 1986. *Annual Report.* Glasgow, Loch Lomond Angling Improvement Association.
Mackay Consultants, 1989. *The economic importance of salmon fishing and netting in Scotland.* Edinburgh, Scottish Tourist Board.
Maitland, P.S. 1962. *Bathynella natans,* new to Scotland. *Glasgow Naturalist* 18, 175-176.
Maitland, P.S. 1972. Loch Lomond: man's effects on the salmonid community. *Journal of the Fisheries Research Board of Canada* 29, 849-860.
Maitland, P.S. 1980. Scarring of Whitefish (*Coregonus lavaretus*) by European River Lamprey (*Lampetra fluviatilis*) in Loch Lomond, Scotland. *Canadian Journal of Fisheries and Aquatic Science* 37, 1981-1988.
Maitland, P.S. 1983. Loch Lomond's unique fish community. *Scottish Wildlife* 19, 23-26.
Maitland, P.S. 1984. The effects of eutrophication on wildlife. *Institute of Terrestrial Ecology Symposium* 13, 101-108.
Maitland, P.S. 1990. Pike in Loch Lomond. *Discover Scotland* 27, 756.
Maitland, P.S. 2001. *A bibliography of published work concerning the fresh waters of the Loch Lomond and the Trossachs National Park.* Battleby, Scottish Natural Heritage.
Maitland, P.S. and East, K. 1989. An increase in numbers of Ruffe, *Gymnocephalus cernua* (L.), in a Scottish loch from 1982 to 1987. *Aquaculture and Fisheries Management* 20, 227-228.
Maitland, P.S., East, K. and Morris, K.H. 1983. Ruffe *Gymnocephalus cernua* (L.), new to Scotland, in Loch Lomond. *Scottish Naturalist* 1983, 7-9.
Maitland, P.S. and Lyle, A.A. 1991. Conservation of freshwater fish in the British Isles: the current status and biology of threatened species. *Aquatic Conservation* 1, 25-54.
Maitland, P.S., Lyle, A.A. and Campbell, R.N.B. 1987. *Acidification and fish populations in Scottish lochs.* Grange-over Sands, Institute of Terrestrial Ecology.
Maitland, P.S., Newson, M.D. and Best, G.E. 1990. *The impact of afforestation and forestry practice on freshwater habitats.* Peterborough, Nature Conservancy Council.
Maitland, P.S. and Smith, I.R. 1987. The River Tay: ecological changes from source to estuary. *Proceedings of the Royal Society of Edinburgh* 91B, 373-392.
Slack, H.D. 1965. The profundal fauna of Loch Lomond. *Proceedings of the Royal Society of Edinburgh* 69, 272-297.
Smith, B.D., Maitland, P.S. and Pennock, S.M. 1987. A comparative study of water level regimes and littoral benthic communities in Scottish lochs. *Biological Conservation* 39, 291-316.
SOAFD. 1990. *Freshwater Fisheries Laboratory Annual Review.* Edinburgh, Scottish Office.
TRPB. 1989. *Annual Report.* Perth, Tay River Purification Board.
TRPB. 1990. *Annual Report.* Perth, Tay River Purification Board.

Table 1. Check list of freshwater fish species found in the Loch Lomond and the Trossachs National Park.

COMMON NAME	SCIENTIFIC NAME	STATUS	FREQUENCY
River Lamprey	*Lampetra fluviatilis* (Linnaeus 1758)	N	***
Brook Lamprey	*Lampetra planeri* (Bloch 1784)	N	****
Sea Lamprey	*Petromyzon marinus* Linnaeus 1758	N	**
Common Sturgeon	*Acipenser sturio* Linnaeus 1758	V	*
Eel	*Anguilla anguilla* (Linnaeus 1758)	N	*****
Allis Shad	*Alosa alosa* (Linnaeus 1758)	V	*
Twaite Shad	*Alosa fallax* (Lacepede 1803)	V	*
Common Bream	*Abramis brama* (Linnaeus 1758)	A	*
Goldfish	*Carassius auratus* (Linnaeus 1758)	A	*
Crucian Carp	*Carassius carassius* (Linnaeus 1758)	A	*
Common Carp	*Cyprinus carpio* Linnaeus 1758	A	*
Gudgeon	*Gobio gobio* (Linnaeus 1758)	A	*
Chub	*Leuciscus cephalus* (Linnaeus 1758)	A	*
Orfe	*Leuciscus idus* (Linnaeus 1758)	A	*
Dace	*Leuciscus leuciscus* (Linnaeus 1758)	A	**
Minnow	*Phoxinus phoxinus* (Linnaeus 1758)	N	*****
Roach	*Rutilus rutilus* (Linnaeus 1758)	N	***
Rudd	*Scardinius erythrophthalmus* (Linnaeus 1758)	A	*
Tench	*Tinca tinca* (Linnaeus 1758)	A	*
Stone Loach	*Barbatula barbatula* (Linnaeus 1758)	N	****
Pike	*Esox lucius* Linnaeus 1758	N	***
Powan	*Coregonus lavaretus* (Linnaeus 1758)	N	**
Rainbow Trout	*Oncorhynchus mykiss* (Walbaum 1792)	A	***
Atlantic Salmon	*Salmo salar* Linnaeus 1758	N	****
Brown Trout	*Salmo trutta* Linnaeus 1758	N	*****
Arctic Charr	*Salvelinus alpinus* (Linnaeus 1758)	N	**
Brook Charr	*Salvelinus fontinalis* (Mitchill 1814)	A	*
Grayling	*Thymallus thymallus* (Linnaeus 1758)	A	*
Thick-lipped Grey Mullet	*Chelon labrosus* Risso 1826	N	*
Thin-lipped Grey Mullet	*Liza ramada* (Risso 1826)	N	*
Three-spined Stickleback	*Gasterosteus aculeatus* Linnaeus 1758	N	****
Nine-spined Stickleback	*Pungitius pungitius* (Linnaeus 1758)	N	*
Sea Bass	*Dicentrarchus labrax* (Linnaeus 1758)	N	*
Ruffe	*Gymnocephalus cernuus* (Linnaeus 1758)	A	**
Perch	*Perca fluviatilis* Linnaeus 1758	N	***
Common Goby	*Pomatoschistus microps* (Kroyer 1838)	N	**
Flounder	*Platichthys flesus* (Linnaeus 1758)	N	***

N = Native
A = Alien
V = Vagrant

*=Restricted distribution / Rare
**=Few sites / Uncommon
***=Several sites / Fairly common
****=Many sites / Common
*****=Widespread / Very Common

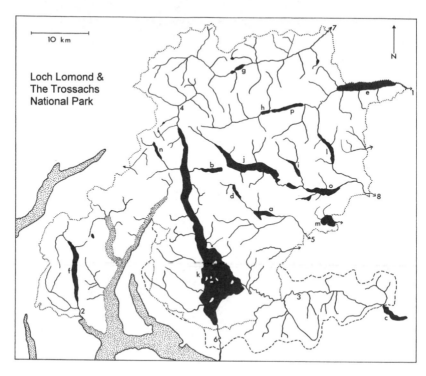

Figure 1. Sketch map showing the waters of the Loch Lomond and the Trossachs National Park area. The boundary of the National Park is a dotted line, that of the Loch Lomond catchment outwith the Park is a dashed line. Sea lochs are stippled. The principal lochs are: (a) Ard, (b) Arklet, (c) Carron Valley, (d) Chon, (e) Earn, (f) Eck, (g) Dochart, (h) Doine, (i) Glen Finglas, (j) Katrine, (k) Lomond, (l) Lubnaig, (m) Menteith, (n) Sloy, (o) Venachar, (p) Voil; and the principal rivers are: (1) Earn, (2) Eachaig, (3) Endrick, (4) Falloch, (5) Forth, (6) Leven, (7) Tay, (8) Teith.

THE BILL BRACKENRIDGE MEMORIAL PROJECT

Wetland Enhancement at Broadwood, Cumbernauld

Brian Thomson

Work is now progressing well on habitat improvements on raised bog and wetland by Broadwood Loch, on the western outskirts of Cumbernauld.

In his time as Ecologist with the Conservation and Greening Unit of North Lanarkshire Council, Broadwood Loch and its surrounds was a favourite haunt of Bill Brackenridge, and together we planned for its further enhancement. Indeed on the day before his untimely death in winter 2000, Bill was out walking the ground at Broadwood drawing up a Phase 1 habitat map, and considering future biodiversity initiatives.

Broadwood Loch was created in the early 1990s by the Cumbernauld Development Corporation as an ambitious amenity scheme, with the open water to act as a back-drop to the new housing at Blackwood, the Broadwood Stadium and the developing business park. In the process significant bog and grassland habitat was eliminated as large volumes of peat and mineral soil were excavated, and then further habitat was lost as this spoil was spread 1.5 to 2 metres deep over half of the raised bog remaining. This then quickly developed a vegetation dominated by rushes and coarse grasses, with only sparse elements of traditional bog vegetation such as *sphagnum* moss and heather having a toe-hold in the area. It is this highly degraded area which has been the main focus of habitat diversification.

This winter contractors have been working to a plan designed to form a series of larger ponds, smaller pools, ditches and mud-scrapes. The biodiversity objectives of the Project include:

- To create breeding and feeding refuges for Teal, Mallard and Little Grebe.
- To eliminate public access to the shoreline in this area and form pools and mudscrapes for the significant population of wintering Snipe and nesting waterfowl, including Mute Swan and Great-Crested Grebe.
- To create pools and ditches on mineral soil and on peaty soil to diversify breeding Odonata populations. Target species are Four-spotted Chaser, Azure Damselfly, Emerald Damselfly, and Common Hawker Dragonfly, all of which breed in North Lanarkshire.
- Pools and ponds as habitats for amphibian populations. Target species are Common Frogs and Palmate Newts.
- To diversify the vegetation by establishing a fine-grass heath community over the excavated spoil from the large ponds, and on wetter ground by introducing wetland and waterside plants including Ragged Robin, Yellow Flag Iris, and Purple Loosestrife.
- To introduce specific vegetation which may in the future attract and support breeding butterfly populations. Target species are Marsh Violet and Small Pearl-bordered Fritillary (a North Lanarkshire LBAP priority

which used to occur at Broadwood before its habitat was lost by the Loch formation); Cuckoo Flower for Orange-Tip; Sheep's Sorrel for Small Copper; and Birds Foot Trefoil for Common Blue.

- On the adjacent intact raised bog to remove invading birch and pine seedlings, and block drains as and where required.

The pond work is completed, wildflower seed mixes due to be sown, and volunteer conservation days in April and May helped plant up the hundreds of potted wildflowers. All who donated to the Memorial Fund, and those who helped practically, attended an 'open day' to launch the Project on 21st June at Broadwood Stadium; a buffet and slide show was followed by a site tour. The future looks promising.

Editor's note: This report is presented by courtesy of the BRISC Newsletter, and very relevant are brief introductions to another four 'Wild green spaces of Cumbernauld' in SWT's *Scottish Wildlife* Autumn '02 pp30-31.

EDITORIAL NOTES

Contents and Index to *The Forth Naturalist and Historian*, volumes 16-24, 1993-2001. 22pp now available £1.00 plus 50p p&p.

Previous indexes were – volumes 1-5, 1975-80; 1982; 6-10, 1981-8, 1989; 11-15, 1989-1992, 1993.

Back issues of the Journal ... all plus £1 p&p if posted.
Volumes now 'out of print' are – 1-7, 9-11, 13, 14, 17
Volumes available at just £1 each – 8, 16, 19
Volumes available at just £2 each – 21, 22, 23
Volumes available at full price of £6 – 24, 25

Bob McCutcheon – FNH Board member, outstanding Stirling man, local historian, bookseller, genealogist, friend, is sadly, at just 62, taken away from us by ill health. Many attended the distinctive funeral services on Thursday 5th September at Bannockburn Community Centre and Bannockburn cemetery.

For our late naturalist Board member Bill Brackenridge a commemorative project (see the Thomson paper) is ongoing, something similarly commemorative is expected for Bob by the community.

Forthcoming
Papers are anticipated on – Lampreys; Fleas of Clackmannanshire; Bridge of Allan hydro; early Gartmore; and Torwood.

Author Addresses
Andrew Ashbee, WEA Musica Britannica, University of Kent, Canterbury.
Ishbel Barnes, National Archives of Scotland, Edinburgh, EH1 3YT – retired.
Priscilla Bawcutt, English Language and Literature, University of Liverpool, L69 7ZR
Richard Fawcett, Historic Scotland, Salisbury Place, Edinburgh, EH9 1SH.
John Harrison, St John's, 129 Main St, Spittal, Berwick-upon-Tweed, TD15 1RP.
C.J. Henty, Psychology, University of Stirling, FK9 4LA.
Joanna Laynesmith, Pembroke College, Oxford, OX1 1DW.
Norman Macdougall, Scottish History, University of St Andrews, KY16 9AL – retired
Ken Mackay, Hayford House, Cambusbarron, FK7 9PR.
Peter Maitland, Fish Conservation Centre, Gladshot, Haddington, EH41 4NR.
John Mitchell, 22 Muirpark Way, Drymen, G63 0DX.
Michael Penman, History, University of Stirling, FK9 4LA.
David Perry, 2 Inchna, Menstrie, FK11 7HP.
David Spooner, 96 Halbeath Road, Dunfermline, KY12 7LR.
Louis Stott, 10 Trossachs Road, Aberfoyle, FK8 3SW.
Brian Thomson, N Lanark, Conservation and Greening, Palacerigg House, Cumbernauld, G67 3HU.

BOOK REVIEWS

Biosphere reserves: Special places for people and nature. UNESCO. 2002. 210pp. ISBN 92 3 103813 3. £14.50.

The biosphere reserve concept was launched in the mid-1970s as part of UNESCO's international programme on Man and the Biosphere (MAB), a practical field approach to combining the conservation of biological diversity with the needs of sustainable development.

There are ten substantive illustrated chapters including the objectives of the Seville Strategy adopted in 1995. Varieties of forests – tropical, rain, temperate; grasslands; deserts; wetlands; mountain and highlands. Conservation. Sustainable development. Extensive bibliography and index.

P189 quotes for SNH, 9 UK sites – Ben Eight, Braunton Burroughs, Cairnsmore of Fleet, Dyfi, Loch Druidibeg, Moor House Upper Teesdale, N Norfolk Coast, Silver Flowe-Merrick Kells, Claish Moss, Taynish!!

Fishes in Estuaries. Editors M. Elliott and K.L. Hemingway. Blackwell Science. 580pp. ISBN 0 632 05733 5. £45.

This work brings together, European wide, scientists collating their ongoing and previous studies, and leading academics and government, and providing a database of information and expertise on all aspects of the biology and management of fishes in estuarine habitats – including – nurseries and feeding grounds, saltmarshes, reed beds, seagrass marshes, sand and mudflats – for commercial fish and shellfish species.

Note two articles of interest in the *Scots Magazine* of April 2002 –
Drawn to Nature: Polly Pullar presents a profile of wildlife artist and naturalist, Keith Brockie. pp345-350. Brockie is noted for his work with eagles, ospreys, hares.
Our Fabulous Ferns. Gregory Kenicer. pp366-370.

THE THISTLE AND THE ROSE

Michael Penman

A conference to commemorate the 500th anniversary
of the Treaty of Perpetual Peace 1502-13

Introduction

On Saturday 23rd March 2002 a one-day conference was held by the
Department of History at the University of Stirling. This was held to coincide
with the splendid exhibition opened by the Princess Royal at Stirling castle a
few days earlier and organised by Historic Scotland and the National Library
of Scotland to commemorate the anniversary of the betrothal of James IV of
Scotland to Margaret Tudor, daughter of Henry VII of England. Their resulting
marriage at Holyrood in August 1503 and its allied 'treaty of perpetual peace'
have long been seen as marking a crucial moment in Anglo-Scottish relations.
It is thus an event worthy of celebration and illustration in the twenty-first
century to echo the celebrations of the Scottish and English courtiers of the
early sixteenth century, not least the words of Scots poet William Dunbar
whose famous verse gives both the exhibition and conference their name.

Six expert scholars came together to re-examine the political context,
personalities and cultural background to this momentous match: each gave
highly informed, entertaining and persuasive papers, very well-received by an
audience of some ninety people, many of them members of local history
groups like the Clackmannanshire Field Studies Society and the Marie Stuart
Society. The Forth Naturalist and Historian was kind enough to contribute to
the funding of the conference as were the Faculty of Arts and the Alumni Fund
of the University: to all these bodies many thanks. In the end, it was not
possible to publish all of the papers given but the opening talk of the
conference by Dr Norman Macdougall on the political background to the
marriage is reproduced below, followed by synopses of the remaining five
papers, guides to further reading and a list of the contents of the castle
exhibition. It is hoped to publish the day's proceedings in full (with
illustrations) at a later date. The organisers of the conference would like to
thank the six speakers for all their tremendous hard work and to thank all
those who attended for their support – it was much appreciated. The
Department of History hopes to organise similar one-day conferences of local
interest in the near future, including *Reputations in Scottish History* (planned for
June 2003) – an examination of the changing historical and popular images of
key Scottish national icons – as well as, perhaps, a re-evaluation of the reign of
Robert I.

The 1502 Treaty of Perpetual Peace – English version – with portraits of James IV and Margaret Tudor. (Illustration by courtesy of Historic Scotland and National Archives of Scotland.)

THE POLITICAL CONTEXT OF THE PERPETUAL PEACE (1502)

Norman Macdougall

The Anglo-Scottish peace of 1502, and the marriage of 1503, are rarely discussed without reference to the events of a century later. Time and again, from school text books to scholarly monographs, the 1502-3 marriage treaty is seen almost as a prelude to union, with the Stewart-Tudor marriage leading eventually to James IV's great-grandson succeeding to the English throne in 1603 and so fulfilling, well ahead of time, Dr. Johnson's famous maxim that the fairest road ever seen by a Scotsman is the high road that leads to England. In this interpretation of events, the union of the thistle and the rose plays a modest role in leading the Scots towards their inevitable and desirable destiny, absorption within a British state. A pity, then, that James IV sought to spoil the march of progress by reneging on the 1502 English treaty only eleven years after it was made, for which backsliding he was quite properly defeated and killed at Flodden in September 1513.

But reading history backwards rather than forwards is a dangerous game; for it is at once apparent that the succession of a Scottish king to the English throne in 1603 was not an obvious outcome of the thistle-rose marriage of 1503, but rather the unlikely result of a century-long see-saw of Tudor and Stewart diplomatic upsets, births, premature deaths, and infant mortality. Best, therefore, to forget 1603 and to focus instead on the context of the 1502 Treaty of Perpetual Peace, bearing in mind distinction between what happens and what is actually going on.

What happens in 1502-3 is clear enough. At the beginning of August 1503 Margaret Tudor, elder daughter of King Henry VII of England, entered south-east Scotland en route for her wedding with James IV. The bride was thirteen, her husband thirty, and the wedding, at Holyrood Abbey, adjoining King James's newly constructed Renaissance palace, on 8 August, was marked by lavish expenditure on the part of the Scottish king, including more than £2,000 Scots on wine alone. The wedding festivities, which included Margaret Tudor's formal entry into Edinburgh together with five days of minstrelsy, tournaments, dancing, and the creation of new earls and knights by the king, were recorded at length by John Young, the English Somerset Herald, and the event is perhaps best known through the celebratory poem by the Scots court poet William Dunbar, 'The Thrissil and the Rose'.

The 1503 wedding was the cornerstone of the much-lauded Anglo-Scottish Treaty of Perpetual Peace, concluded in January 1502. As its grandiose title suggests, this was a full-scale alliance containing elaborate rules for the maintenance of peace, papal approval and confirmation, together with the threat of excommunication should either monarch break the treaty. More practically, Margaret Tudor's dowry was set at 30,000 Angel nobles (about £35,000 Scots) to be paid to James IV in three annual instalments.

So much for what happened. But what was going on? It is sometimes forgotten that the treaty of 1502 was not the first of its kind; a generation earlier, in October 1474, James IV's father James III had concluded a marriage alliance with the Yorkist Edward IV of England. Uniquely among late medieval Scottish kings, James III consistently sought English truces and alliances over a period of fourteen years, with Edward IV, Richard III, and with the Tudor Henry VII. None of the projected marriages was ever realised; and the Scottish king's obsequious pursuit of alliances which were peripheral to England's diplomatic interests left him dangerously exposed at home without much hope of English intervention on his behalf. In June 1488 he was overwhelmed and killed at or after the battle of Sauchieburn near Stirling; and his fifteen-year-old son, the nominal leader of the rebels, became king as James IV.

At first sight, the new king appears a highly unlikely candidate as signatory to a Treaty of Perpetual Peace with England. Having removed his Anglophile father, James IV's early governments moved swiftly to find a European bride for the young king. A high-powered embassy led by Patrick Hepburn, earl of Bothwell, the king's guardian, and including – perhaps – the poet William Dunbar, who distinguished himself by being violently seasick before the ship had got further than the Bass Rock – sailed to France in the summer of 1491; the Scottish ambassadors made their way to the French court at Tours on the Loire, where they were presented to the French king, Charles VIII, by Bérault Stewart, lord of Aubigny, the most influential Franco-Scot in the service of the French crown, and the architect of the recent Franco-Scottish treaty of 1484. However, a proposal that James IV should marry Blanche, daughter of Giangaleazzo Sforza of Milan, was vetoed by the French king; and though a renewal of the 'auld alliance' was effected early in 1492, there was no French bride available for the Scottish king. Subsequent endeavours to make a matrimonial alliance in the Holy Roman Empire and Spain, in the pursuit of which James IV employed bishop Elphinstone of Aberdeen and archbishop Blacader of Glasgow respectively, proved abortive by 1496.

There remained the English alternative; but the eventual marriage of 1503 was only achieved as the result of extremely aggressive diplomacy, and ultimately war, on the part of the Scots. While James IV was still a minor, in May 1493, Henry VII of England had been prepared only to offer Katharine, daughter of Eleanor, countess of Wiltshire, as a prospective bride for the king of Scots – not much of a catch for a king whose father and grandfather had respectively married the daughters of the rulers of Gueldres and Denmark.

In the spring of 1495, however, James IV took personal control of his government. At age 22 a late developer by Stewart standards, he soon showed himself a ruler of remarkable skill and subtlety; and he began by raising the English marriage stakes and looking for the hand of Henry VII's daughter Margaret Tudor. Faced with English prevarication, if not outright refusal, James IV adopted the high risk policy of making war on England, using the much-travelled Yorkist pretender to Henry VII's throne, Perkin Warbeck, as his excuse. James IV's real motives were to bring pressure to bear on Henry VII to part with his daughter, to make effective use of the often factious Scottish nobility in a productive war, and to force the English king to recognise Scotland's status as a formidable player in European diplomacy. The Spanish ambassador to Scotland, Don Pedro de Ayala, travelled with James IV on his campaigns into Northumberland in 1496 and 1497, and remarked of the king:

> 'He is courageous, even more so than a king should be. I am a good witness of it. I have seen him often undertake most dangerous things in the last wars. I sometimes clung to his skirts and succeeded in keeping him back. On such occasions he does not take the least care of himself . . . I can say with truth that he esteems himself as much as though he were lord of the world. He loves war . . .'

King James's military objective, apart from giving the Scottish army the pleasure of attacking 'soft' targets in the Tweed and Till valleys, was the Bishop of Durham's great castle of Norham, just south of the river Tweed where it forms the Anglo-Scottish border. He used the castle as target practice for his artillery, including the great Burgundian cannon Mons Meg, but sensibly withdrew from the siege on the approach of an English army under the Earl of Surrey. Henry VII, normally a cautious and devious ruler, had already been provoked into furious revenge; but the heavy taxes which he demanded to pursue a Scottish war helped to provoke a major rising in Cornwall, an event so serious that the Cornish rebels got to within 20 miles of London before they were defeated. Henry VII recovered his diplomatic poise, and sought his own security in peace with Scotland. Don Pedro de Ayala went south as James IV's ambassador in October 1497, and in the following year remarked that he had been the main instrument of Anglo-Scottish peace. In England, he said, he was looked on as remarkable because he could hear the word 'Scotland' pronounced without losing his temper; and he added that only King James sought peace with England, which was made against the wishes of the majority of his subjects. Thus the peace of 1502, and the royal marriage of August 1503, were not the result of a spontaneous outburst of Anglo-Scottish amity. They were arrived at *faut de mieux* by two kings who had first investigated other possibilities and then fought each other to a stand-still in an expensive and inconclusive war.

Even before James IV married his daughter in 1503, Henry VII had deep concerns about one possible outcome of the treaty. Three months after it was concluded, in April 1502, Henry's eldest son Arthur died without heirs; and the following February his queen, Elizabeth, also died. King Henry had, of course, a second son who would eventually succeed as Henry VIII; but these rapid deaths suddenly made the prospect of a Scottish succession to the English throne appear much more than a remote possibility. Hence Henry VII's growing insecurity, and his letter to James IV on 27 June 1503 – about six weeks before the Edinburgh wedding – asking the Scottish king to repudiate the Franco-Scottish alliance, or at least not to renew it with Louis XII, who had come to the French throne in 1498. James IV replied promptly on 12 July, remarking that, as regards the French alliance, 'we and our predecessors have been always accustomed thereto'; but he promised not to confirm the league with France without first notifying Henry – not much of a concession.

It may be argued, then, that the Treaty of Perpetual Peace was of greater value to James IV than to his new father-in-law King Henry. It gave the Scottish king added security, but did not deny him a certain flexibility in his future foreign policy; for he had no intention of repeating the obsequiousness of his father James III towards the English king, and by pursuing French connections after 1502 as before it, James IV was able to satisfy his own countrymen and present a united front to Scotland's only potential enemy. Even a casual glance at King James's published correspondence with foreign governments and individuals associated with them reveals that he sent three times as much diplomatic mail to France and Denmark as to England; and it does not appear that the Anglo-Scottish treaty of 1502 worked for any length of time in reducing tension and conflict in areas where friction was always to be expected, on the borders and at sea.

As early as August 1505, little over a month after the payment of the third and final instalment of Margaret Tudor's dowry to the Scots, Henry VII received reports that the Scots would invade Northumberland and lay siege to the east coast burgh of Berwick, lost to the English as recently as 1482. In fact, no invasion took place; and wisely, James IV made no attempt to recapture Berwick, even during his successful 1496 and 1497 campaigns, which brought him within a few miles of the burgh. Indeed, Berwick has remained English since its capture in 1482. Although nothing came of the Berwick rumours of 1505, King Henry's fears of a formal renewal of the Franco-Scottish alliance of 1492 increased as the years passed; and in the spring of 1508 there occurred an incident which casts a revealing light on James IV's domination of his council and his devious diplomatic techniques.

The occasion was the arrest by Henry VII of King James's ambassador and kinsman, James Hamilton, earl of Arran, on a technicality – he had been passing through England without a safe-conduct. This unusually precipitate move by Henry VII seems to have been caused by fears that Arran was involved in preparing the way for a renewal of the Franco-Scottish alliance; and to forestall this, King Henry not only detained Arran in England but sent north his young and able almoner Thomas Wolsey, a royal servant in the early stages of what was to develop into a spectacular career, to negotiate with King James.

Wolsey reached the border at Berwick on 22 March 1508, and was kept waiting for five days for a safe-conduct to enter Scotland; James IV, he was told, was on pilgrimage at Whithorn. When Wolsey finally reached Edinburgh at the end of the month, he was informed that the king would not see him for another week, because he was busy shooting and making gunpowder. Finally admitted into the royal presence, Wolsey attempted to put the English case against Scottish subjects passing through England without safe-conducts, but was met with considerable hostility. As for the Franco-Scottish alliance, James

IV wanted to impress on Wolsey that its renewal was imminent; all his subjects, he said, called upon him daily to renew the alliance; and the entire royal council trooped in to underline the point. Even Andrew Forman, bishop of Moray and one of the original architects of the 1502 English treaty, took Wolsey aside and told him that no-one was ever less welcome in Scotland, because it was generally believed that he had come to prevent a renewal of the French league. With heavy irony, Wolsey commented that the Scots 'keep their matters so secret ... that the wives in the market knoweth every cause of my coming'. But this elaborate piece of diplomatic theatre had the desired effect. Wolsey came away from Scotland convinced that a wide spectrum of Scottish political opinion was firmly united behind the king, and that only the release of the Earl of Arran would keep James from renewing the French league. Arran was promptly released.

King James kept to his word. He did not renew the Franco-Scottish alliance in 1508. But then he did not need to do so, for Franco-Scottish amity was already well established. Only a few weeks after Wolsey's departure, Bérault Stewart, Lord of Aubigny, returned to Scotland for the first time since 1484, when he had negotiated a renewal of the Auld Alliance with James III. Stewart, who was heading a French embassy, received a tumultuous welcome; gifts were showered on him, and James IV wrote to Louis XII asking permission to keep the Lord of Aubigny in Scotland long enough to visit Whithorn on pilgrimage in his company, a pilgrimage which Bérault Stewart had vowed to make, and which 'will actually enable so trusty a man to inform James thoroughly regarding his commission'. A spectacular joust was held at Holyrood in Stewart's honour in May 1508, with James IV taking an active part. The Lord of Aubigny survived the lists but died of an unknown illness at Corstorphine near Edinburgh on 11 June. Perhaps significantly, one of his last acts had been to write a treatise on war. His chivalric virtues were duly extolled in a poem by William Dunbar, and James IV, in a spate of letters to Louis XII, recalled his 'famous and dear kinsman' and revealed his enthusiasm for the Franco-Scottish alliance – without, however, seeking its formal renewal.

It is, of course, easy to draw attention to the disadvantages of the Scottish alliance with France, by this time more than two centuries old. Successive French kings, it is claimed, looked to the Scots simply as cannon fodder for diversionary raids on northern England, regularly abandoning their allies when it suited France to end hostilities with England. Undoubtedly this happened; but the connection with France meant far more to the participants than oft-repeated offensive and defensive treaties directed against England. To large numbers of Scots, France was a land flowing with milk and honey, offering opportunities beyond their wildest dreams at home – in the early fifteenth century the dukedom of Touraine for the Earls of Douglas, the constableship of France for an earl of Buchan; and rather later, the lordship of Concressault for Sir William Monypenny, and that of Aubigny for Stewart of Darnley. Likewise, France offered spectacular careers in the church for individuals like Master John Kirkmichael, bishop of Orléans when the city was relieved by Joan of Arc in 1429; Robert Cockburn, who combined the thankless post of bishop of Ross with the highly remunerative one of chaplain to Louis XII of France; and the most dramatic case of all was that of Andrew Forman, bishop of Moray, one of the principal Scottish architects of the English peace of 1502. For this diplomatic achievement, Forman was rewarded with no more than the rectory of Cottingham in Yorkshire by a miserly Henry VII; but ten years later, having shifted his ground to pursuit of the Franco-Scottish alliance, Forman did much, much better, receiving the archbishopric of Bourges through the offices of a grateful Louis XII.

Apart from these high fliers, large numbers of Scots were to be found throughout later medieval France, as scholars in the universities of Paris and Orléans, or as mercenary soldiers in the service of the Crown. In September 1513, Louis XII, recalling the long and close alliance between France and Scotland, stretching back to the days of Charles VII – who had chosen 200 Scots to be his bodyguard – granted all Scots resident in France the privilege of disposing of their goods by will without having to apply for letters of naturalisation.

For Scots who remained at home, above all James IV himself, the French connection was at least as valuable. The national patron saint of Scotland was, and is, St. Andrew, and his emblem, the saltire, is to be found in many varied art forms at this time. In addition, however, the cult of St. Michael, introduced into France in August 1468 by Louis XI (when he founded the knightly order of that name) was enthusiastically taken up by the Scots at the beginning of the sixteenth century; there is no doubt that Louis XII bestowed the Order of St. Michael on James IV probably around 1508-1510. Certainly the close links between France and Scotland are reflected in the appearance of St. Michael, not only in the naming of the great Scottish warship of 1511, but also in the effigy of the saint in the building work on the church of St. Michael at Linlithgow by James IV, and – by implication – in the last gold coinage of the reign in 1513, which carries the representation of a warship, much like the '*Michael*', and bears the legend 'Salvator in Hoc Signo Vicisti' (Saviour by this sign hast thou conquered). Is this perhaps an anticipation of Franco-Scottish victory in the war of 1513 against England?

Further French influence within Scotland is to be seen in the royal patent granted by James IV in September 1507 to Walter Chepman and Andrew Myllar, to establish Scotland's first printing press in Edinburgh. Chepman was a wealthy burgess who provided the money, while Myllar was an expatriate Scot who had already printed books in Rouen. What Myllar brought to Edinburgh, therefore, was a French printing press, run by French printers; and the first Scottish books produced by Myllar were therefore wholly French in design and typography. According to James IV's patent, the new press was intended to print 'mass books and breviaries after the use of our realm'; and the most striking example of this is the Aberdeen Breviary (1509-10), the brainchild of James IV's Keeper of the Privy Seal, William Elphinstone, bishop of Aberdeen. The new breviary has been described as a form of 'liturgical nationalism'; for in supplanting the English Sarum (Salisbury) breviary in

Scotland and immortalising around seventy Scottish saints, the Aberdeen Breviary also served the important political function of stressing the independence of the Scottish church, by implication denying the claims to ecclesiastical overlordship which were occasionally advanced by the English archdiocese of York.

Thus in patronising Scotland's first printing press, as in so much else, James IV was moved by political and diplomatic considerations, by growing hostility to England and by the strengthening of ties with France. It may be added that King James continued to have links with Rouen, the original source of the Chepman/Myllar press; for in 1510 the Scottish king commissioned a satire *Les abus du monde*, by Pierre Gringoire, a work which was published in Rouen. Gringoire's career is in itself significant, for he was an immensely popular comic writer and poet who took a strongly partisan line in France's foreign affairs, attacking in satirical terms all of Louis XII's enemies for more than a decade. Gringoire was eventually rewarded with the composition and production of all seven spectacles in the Renaissance pageant which accompanied the entry into Paris of Louis XII's third wife, Mary Tudor, in November 1514. It is tempting to associate Louis XII's ally and Gringoire's other royal patron, James IV of Scotland, with an interest in Renaissance spectacles acquired from France, and perhaps reflecting and informing his own pageants, for example the royal wedding of 1503 and the Holyrood tournaments of 1507 and 1508.

Yet by far the most important aspect of the Franco-Scottish connection during the reigns of these two kings concerned neither pageantry nor propaganda, but war. In August 1506 James IV wrote to Louis XII remarking that the building of a fleet to defend Scotland was a project of long standing; he promised the French king that the Scots fleet would go anywhere Louis wished in his service; and it is surely significant that the building of a Scottish royal fleet began in the autumn of 1502, the year of Scotland's treaty with England. King James, as we have seen, was bound by the most solemn oaths to the alliance with the English; but the treaty gave him a loophole to the effect that, as long as he did not invade England, James might help to defend the territories of any princes who were at war with England without breaking the alliance. In the case of the Scots, this was likely to mean France; and indeed running like a *leitmotif* through all King James's naval plans, ship construction, outfitting, and projected use of his growing fleet, is the Scottish king's close relationship with France and its king, Louis XII. The Scottish fleet – by far the largest royal financial commitment of the reign – was planned by French specialists, largely built by French shipwrights, using large quantities of French timber, and ultimately financed by French money. In Scotland itself, the creation of a royal navy meant job creation on a large scale – new naval dockyards at Pool of Airth near Kincardine-on-Forth, and at Newhaven, where an entire shipbuilding community was created for the purpose of constructing what was – briefly – the largest warship in northern Europe, the *'Michael'*, probably the creation of James IV's master shipwright Jacques Terrell, a ship which, as Louis XII remarked in 1513, was 'si puissante qui ne s'en treuve une telle en chrestiente' (so powerful that we do not find another like it in all Christianity).

At sea as on land, James IV took a very aggressive view of the defence of his country. His construction of a fleet with French aid in the years following 1502 may be seen as an alternative foreign policy, the maintenance of a valuable connection with France while not becoming too heavily involved in France's affairs. Probably this diplomatic balancing act would have been impossible to sustain indefinitely. That war came within a decade was largely the result of the accession to the English throne, in April 1509, of the eighteen-year-old Henry VIII, in Professor Nicholson's words 'an egocentric teenager whose tantrums and petulance bespoke an inferiority complex' [*Scotland: the Later Middle Ages*, 1974]. Shortly after his coronation, the new English king boasted of his intention to invade France, and, when it came, his expedition of summer 1513 was an absurd effort to take advantage of a papal assault on France to restart the Hundred Years' War. With the adherence of King Henry to Pope Julius II's 'Holy League' against France in 1511 and the ensuing Anglo-French war, James IV opted – at last – for a renewal of the Franco-Scottish alliance in March 1512. That he did so is not surprising, for it was to Louis XII that James looked for ships, for munitions, for money to victual his own ships and pay his seamen and James must also have been influenced by the actions of the English parliament, which in January 1512 had not only voted a subsidy for the French war, but declared that the Scottish king was Henry VIII's vassal. But King James was no fool; he would choose his own time for making war on England – not 1512, as the French had wanted and expected – but the summer of 1513, after he had extracted from Louis XII a substantial material offer – 50,000 francs (about £22,500 Scots), together with the French king's agreement to equip and victual the Scottish fleet. Both these commitments were honoured by the French. As for James IV himself, in terms of up-to-date weaponry, he was better supplied than any previous Scottish king; and there has never been such unanimity of support for war amongst the Scots at any time in their history.

Late in July 1513, James IV simultaneously summoned the Scottish host and despatched the fleet carrying his 'armée de mer' – possibly as many as 4,000 men – to France via the Hebrides and an assault on Carrickfergus, the principal English stronghold in Ulster. The combined Scottish, Norman, and Breton fleets, under the command of Louis de Rouville, together with the war galleys of Louis XII's formidable Mediterranean admiral, Gaston Prégent de Bidoux, were then intended, as the French king put it, to 'faire quelque bonne exécucion sur mes ennemys' – possibly to launch a direct assault on Henry VIII's transports at Calais, to prevent the English king from returning safely home from Picardy in the autumn. Like most Grand Designs in war, this one did not succeed; but initially it appeared that James IV's invasion of Northumberland, late in August 1513, would be much more successful. A huge army crossed the Tweed, and King James in person laid siege to the bishop of Durham's great stronghold of Norham. After five days it was taken by storm, and the bishop remarked in a letter to Wolsey that he would never recover from the shock, a state of mind in which he remained for rather less than a fortnight.

For on Branxton Hill on the wet and windy afternoon of 9 September, James IV, rashly employing Swiss or 'Almayn' tactics – the rapid movement of huge phalanxes of spearmen – on unsuitable terrain, fatally encountered an English army of similar size under Thomas Howard, earl of Surrey, and was killed together with a huge array of his magnates and rank-and-file troops. This carnage, later described as the battle of Flodden, caused this most successful of all late medieval Scottish kings to suffer the death which had always been an occupational risk for a ruler who habitually led his armies from the front.

In spite of its tragic consequences, James IV's war makes sense in a way in which Henry VIII's excursion into France does not. Duped and then deserted by his shifty allies, frittering away his father's huge legacy, hopelessly out of his depth in the morass of European diplomacy, the English king not only missed the only major engagement of the war, but ended up making peace with, and marrying his younger sister to, Louis XII, whose kingdom he had earlier claimed for himself.

To conclude: James IV has been much criticised over the years for his supposed diplomatic incompetence following 1502; but I should like to suggest that that criticism should apply only to his military ineptitude on the last day of his life. Flodden was not the inevitable result of James's entry into the war of 1513 on France's side, still less of his diplomacy throughout the preceding decade. Indeed, as this paper has tried to show, that diplomacy was the work of an able, calculating ruler, and was broadly successful. James IV had used war in the 1490s to force Henry VII into putting his elder daughter on the marriage market. Once the Perpetual Peace of 1502 was made, the Scottish king changed tack, picked up the threads of the French alliance once more, and ran both alliances until they became incompatible. When the crunch came, he opted not for an extension of the ten years of Perpetual Peace, but rather for a renewal of the two hundred and seventeen years of Auld Alliance, not out of sentiment, but because the French king offered him substantial material inducements.

So how then should we celebrate the Anglo-Scottish treaty of 1502 in its quincentenary year? Certainly it brought to both signatories a decade of uneasy peace; and of course there is the famous marital union of 1503, with its far-off and unlikely outcome, to delight the sensibilities of enthusiasts for British history. Beyond that, however, the treaty can hardly be regarded as a success in improving early Stewart-Tudor relations. Indeed, the construction of gun emplacements at the Queensferry narrows on the Forth, and on Inchgarvie island halfway across, the probable installation of guns on Ailsa Craig in the Clyde, the new naval dockyards on the Forth, the abandonment of Berwick but extensive reconstruction of Dunbar castle, and the building of a Scottish royal navy with French aid – all these schemes tell a very different story, suggesting a consistent, integrated Scottish royal defensive and offensive strategy directed against the only kingdom, as even James III had noted, which ever made war on Scotland. In terms of Anglo-Scottish relations, then, 1502 changed very little; and paradoxically its immediate outcome – aided, it must be said, by some remarkably inept English diplomacy – was the renewal and enhancement of the Franco-Scottish alliance for the following half-century.

Recommended further reading:

N. Barr, *Flodden 1513*, Tempus, Stroud, 2001; S.B. Chrimes, *Henry VII*, Eyre Methuen, London, 1972; M. Lynch, *Scotland: A New History*, Pimlico, London, 1991; N. Macdougall, *James III: A Political Study*, John Donald, Edinburgh, 1982.; N. Macdougall, *James IV*, 2nd edition, Tuckwell Press, East Linton, 1997; N. Macdougall, *An Antidote to the English: The Auld Alliance, 1295-1560*, Tuckwell Press, East Linton, 2001; N. Macdougall, " 'The Greattest Scheip that ewer saillit in Ingland or France': James IV's 'Great Michael' ", in N. Macdougall ed., *Scotland and War, AD 79-1918*, John Donald, Edinburgh, 1991, 36-60; R.L. Mackie, *King James IV of Scotland: A Brief Survey of his Life and Times*, Oliver & Boyd, Edinburgh, 1958; R.L. Mackie ed., *The Letters of James the Fourth, 1505-1513*, Scottish History Society, Edinburgh, 1953; R. Nicholson, *Scotland: The Later Middle Ages*, Mercat, Edinburgh, 1974; J.J. Scarisbrick, *Henry VIII*, Eyre & Spottiswoode, London, 1968.

The Scottish 'Treaty'.

STEWART AND TUDOR COURT CULTURE: LITERATURE

Priscilla Bawcutt

This paper reflected upon literary culture in Scotland and England about 1500 with particular attention to Scottish poets and the work of William Dunbar, author of 'The Thrissil and the Rose' commemorating the marriage of James IV and Margaret Tudor in 1503. This period was in many ways a 'Golden Age' of Scottish literature in both Scots and Latin, penned not merely by the traditional big three – Dunbar, Robert Henryson and Gavin Douglas – but also by a host of lesser literary figures, many now unidentifiable. These men were usually trained clergymen or lawyers, often serving at the royal court while their literary output formed a secondary role.

Despite the diplomatic and military background, Anglo-Scottish cultural relations in this period may be characterised as 'amicable' based upon the interchange of travel, education and printed book sales as well as a shared historical interest in similar works: medieval chivalric romances, allegorical dream poems, works about the Cult of Honour and of moral and political instruction (advice to princes – *speculum principis*) as well as humanist classical texts. But although Scottish and English (and French) literary works of this period shared many roots and features, Scottish works also had distinct characteristics: an open tone of familiarity and even criticism directed at the crown; a preference for alliterative verse romances (while England preferred prose); a much more skillful 'ease and fluency' of metre and a greater quality of story-telling. Overall, Scotland's literature was 'far more distinguished' than England's in this period.

Much of the literature of this period was written to mark royal occasions like marriages, births and deaths. Several works were written to mark the journey of Margaret Tudor to Scotland and her wedding to James IV at Holyrood in August 1503 (including 'Gladethe, thou quene of Scottis regioun', an unstudied work contained in the 16th century manuscript of the *Liber Pluscardensis*, now held in Glasgow's Mitchell Library). William Dunbar's poem (given its famous title only in the 18th century) is at once a celebratory, allegorical and instructive work of about 200 lines in Scots. Margaret Tudor is symbolised by the rose, crowned by 'Nature' to create an 'ideal garden' of Scotland. But James is also represented in triplicate in the poem: by the Lion and the Eagle – traditional heraldic symbols urged to attend to fair justice – but also by the Thistle, a relatively new emblem signifying the defense of the kingdom and the tending of the allegorical garden of the realm and fidelity to the rose. Designed to be read at court, Dunbar's and other works may also have been presented in formal copy to the royal couple. But the wedding was also marked by pageants and other forms of entertainment, many designed by 'John Inglisch and his companyons'. As with the poetic commemorations, many of these celebrations thus reflected 'the existence of strong bonds between the two countries, in language, literature and culture': for example, in James IV singing to his new bride while accompanied by English players.

Recommended further reading:– P. Bawcutt ed., *The Poems of William Dunbar*, ASLS, Glasgow, 2 volumes, 1998; P. Bawcutt, *Dunbar the Makar*, Oxford, Clarendon, 1992; D. Gray, 'The Royal Entry in Sixteenth Century Scotland', in S. Mapstone and J. Wood eds., *The Rose and the Thistle: Essays on the Culture of late Medieval and Renaissance Scotland*, Tuckwell Press, East Linton, 1998; J. Stevens, *Music and Poetry in the Early Tudor Court*, Lincoln, Nebraska, 1961; W.R. Streitberger, *Court revels 1485-1559*, University of Toronto, 1994.

MUSIC AT THE ENGLISH AND SCOTTISH COURTS *c.*1500
'THE BEST AND MOST JOYFULLEST MANNER'

Andrew Ashbee

This paper surveyed the musicians in the Royal Households and Chapels Royal of Scotland and England *c.* 1500. Much more information is available for musicians at the Tudor court than the Stewart. After 1485, Henry VII organised his Chapel Royal within his Privy Chamber, separate from his Household. The records of these institutions reveal the primary importance of trumpet players with both military and ceremonial court duties, followed by 'shakebushes' or wind players responsible for 'high' formal court music and then 'low' or base music played by minstrels playing rebecs (violins), lutes and harps etc. and accompanying singers. Many of these skilled journeymen musicians traveled from court to court across Europe receiving patronage (and even on occasion working as envoys or spies). But musical accomplishment was also a skill expected of the elite of the day and royal children were taught to play keyboard and lute and to sing.

Important court events were often the occasion of intense musical activity to accompany ceremony and entertainment. Royal marriages in England, for example, often revealed musicians from the foreign partner's court playing to the Tudors and remaining in their employ. What evidence there is of James IV's court music, however, reveals a 'stronger native tradition'. Record survives from 1501 of four (to six) trumpeters, two lutists, four harpists (including a Celtic clarsach and Irish harp players), two 'common pipers' and fiddlers – suggesting the popularity of ballads and folk-music at the Scottish court: no such folk mix was present at the Tudor court until 1511.

But the record of Margaret Tudor's journey to Scotland for her wedding in 1503 reveals both the importance of music at the two royal courts and James' willingness to embrace many forms of playing. Accompanied north by her father, Henry VII, Margaret's departure from England was heralded by choreographed pageants, trumpeters, minstrels and singing. Met by King James at Haddington, there was dancing to minstrel music with James playing to his bride on clavichord and lute as well as singing: Margaret then reciprocated. At Edinburgh a tournament was held before Margaret's formal entry into the town accompanied by pageantry and singing. A High Mass at the Holy Cross kirk followed with members of the Chapel Royal singing there and at the wedding. There was then a banquet with more dancing and playing which lasted a week. In all, James IV paid £105 to English minstrels provided by the English king, his new bride and various English lords present. He also paid four Italian windplayers who would enter his household permanently. James would also have funded his own Chapel Royal based at Stirling castle where he had established a musical college in 1501. It was here that Robert Carver would serve the king by 1513 composing works now recorded in the 'Carver Choir Book' held in the National Library of Scotland, a musical collection which also contains many English works, similar to those found in the main English collections of early sixteenth century court music, the 'Fairfax Manuscript' (British Library) and the 'Eton Choir Book'.

The following illustrative pieces of music were played: *King Harry the Eighth's Pavan*; Cornish: *Adieu my hertes lust*; Spanish/Italian dance: Collinetto; *Helas madame; Fairfax's Aeternae laudis lilium* (written for Queen Elizabeth's visit to St Albans in 1502); Carver's *O Bone Jesu*.

Recommended further reading:— A. Ashbee, ed., *Records of English Court Music*, vols. vii, Snodland, 1993, and viii, Snodland, 1995; *Accounts of the Lords High Treasurer of Scotland, 1473-1580*, vols. i and ii, Edinburgh, 1877-1902; J. Stevens, *Music and Poetry in the Early Tudor Court*, Lincoln, Nebraska, 1961; S. Anglo, *Spectacle Pageantry and Early Tudor Policy*, Oxford, Clarendon, 1969; A. Ashbee & D. Lasocki, *A Biographical Dictionary of English Court Musicians 1485-1714*, Aldershot, Ashgate, 2 vols., 1998; I.W. Preece *et. al.* eds., *'Our uwin Scottis use': Music in the Scottish Church up to 1603*, Univertsities of Glasgow and Aberdeen, 2000; K. Elliot ed., *The Complete Works of Robert Carver*, in *Musica Scotica* vol. I, University of Glasgow, 1996; D.J. Ross, *Musick Fyne: Robert Carver and the Art of Scottish Music in Sixteenth Century Scotland*, Mercat, Edinburgh, 1993.

RENAISSANCE QUEENSHIP

Joanna Laynesmith

This paper examined aspects of the expectations, ideology and practice of queenship *c.* 1500. Margaret Tudor lived in an age when there were many (often contradictory) pressures and duties placed upon young noble and royal women as consorts to kings.

By the late fifteenth century the ideal model for queenship had become the Virgin Mary, 'queen of heaven', a figure which primed the position of queen with great expectations of her role as a benefactor of the church and a peacekeeper and intercessor as well as royal wife, mother and nurse. In addition, the role of queen was a heavily politicised one with royal marriage undertaken for reasons of diplomacy, peacekeeping and acquisition as well as in search of the ideal noble attributes of the day, womanly beauty, virginity and fertility (but not overly so as to cause later disputes). From the viewpoint of the king and kingdom, moreover, a royal marriage and the acquisition of a queen also marked the final maturity of the king and confirmed his sacred authority: the royal bride would be anointed and perhaps crowned alongside her husband while dressed in white and gold and with her hair free, symbolic of the religious feasts of Easter and Christmas and her virginity.

In the course of her betrothal and marriage, Margaret Tudor was subject to many of these expectations of queenship. Contrary to traditional belief she was not baptised in a church dedicated to St Margaret of Scotland and thus not destined from birth to be queen of Scots. Yet despite fears that she was too young to wed and bear children to James IV of Scotland their betrothal went ahead in 1502 when she was 12 and he 29. But the ceremonial rituals of departure which Margaret then underwent in her passage north in 1503 would have been partly familiar to her from her duties as Henry VII's daughter. These rituals lasted three weeks as she progressed to Scotland. There she participated in more choreographed pageantry which reflected her new role as consort of the king of Scots and symbolised her beauty, virginity and sacred role as wife. James met her outside Edinburgh, presented her with a hart and then carried her on horseback through a formal entry into Edinburgh replete with classical and biblical imagery. After their wedding mass Margaret was annointed and presented with a sceptre: she was dressed in white and gold with her hair down while her husband wore garments of similar colour.

Throughout her marriage, Margaret can be found fulfilling a number of expected duties, for example acting as intercessor between James and Henry VIII, bearing six children (of which only one would survive) while wearing a birthing shirt said to have belonged to Scotland's model queen, St Margaret, wife of Malcolm III: in 1507, Margaret also accompanied her husband on pilgrimage to the shrine of St Ninian as his journey there had preceded her recovery from a difficult childbirth. Overall, Margaret was sufficiently trusted as queen to be named guardian for the heir to the throne in the event of James IV's death as long as she did not remarry. She did become guardian after Flodden but lost her political office after her attempts to secure support through remarriage brought criticism from both Scottish and English quarters: her second husband, Archibald Douglas 6th earl of Angus, exerted undue influence over the young James V and Margaret's third marriage after a divorce did not lessen accusations that her loyalties were divided and her morals questionable. This was a double standard often endured by royal women in a male world.

Recommended further reading:– P. Buchanan, *Margaret Tudor, Queen of Scots*, SAP, Edinburgh, 1985; M. Perry, *Sisters to the King*, André Deutsch, London, 1998; L.J. Macfarlane, *William Elphinstone and the Kingdom of Scotland, 1431-1514*, University of Aberdeen, 1985; M. Green, *Lives of the Princesses of England from the Norman Conquest*, vols. iv and v, London, 1849-55; A. Strickland, *Lives of the Queens of Scotland and English Princesses*, vols. i and ii, Edinburgh, 1850-9.

THE BOOK OF HOURS OF JAMES IV AND MARGARET TUDOR, AUSTRIAN NATIONAL LIBRARY, VIENNA

Ishbel Barnes

Books of Hours are a specific type of manuscript which is found from about 1250 onwards. In the Middle Ages the monastic orders followed a programme of daily devotion with Hours or parts of the day set aside for specific religious duties. Mediaeval secular people wanted to follow this in a simplified fashion and from this desire developed what are known as Books of Hours. At their core is the Little Office of Our Lady concentrating on the Virgin. They became a mediaeval best seller and, if they were richly illuminated, a status symbol for the rich. Literally thousands of them still survive.

This lecture discussed one specific Book of Hours – Vienna MS 1897 – and questioned current thinking about the manuscript. Current thinking is that the manuscript was a marriage gift in 1503 from James IV to Margaret Tudor. However problems remain with this conclusion. Contemporary sources do not mention it and it should be found, and isn't, among the detailed expenditures of James IV listed in the Treasurer's Accounts. The textual content of the manuscript also raises problems: important Scottish feast days (like those of St Ninian or St James) which might have been listed in its calendar are missing. The artistic content of the manuscript raises further problems and at least five hands from the Ghent/Bruges associates of artists have been identified as being involved in its production. These attributions can be made on stylistic grounds alone. There is, though, specific Scottish content in the heraldry and portraits.

However, new proposals can be made using later Treasurer's Accounts. In 1502 Thomas Galbraith was paid for illuminating the truce between Scotland and England; in 1505 Andrew Halyburton was paid for providing James IV with a painter from the Low Countries; this painter called "Piers the payntour" was then paid monthly for the following two years. In 1506 he was paid for painting "the Duc of Flandrez arms". In 1507 he was paid for decorations for the tournament which followed the birth of James' first male heir and there was also then given "to the said Pieris, ane buke of gold, gottin and bocht be Schir Thomas Gabreth." In July 1508 "Pieris the payntour" returned to Flanders. It is therefore now suggested that Piers the Painter, like his contemporary the famous Jean Bourdichon at the French court, not only supplied the Scottish court with banners, and portraits etc. but also with this illuminated Book of Hours.

The Austrian Library manuscript was thus perhaps a gift from James IV to Margaret Tudor after the birth of their son in 1507. The work was carried out by Piers the Painter, who may be Pieter van Conixloo, and others including Sir Thomas Galbraith. The work was hurried with illuminations, including the portraits of the king and queen, added in Scotland to the off-the-shelf text purchased in the Low Countries.

Recommended further reading:– L.J. Macfarlane, 'The Book of Hours of James IV and Margaret Tudor', *Innes Review*, xi, 1960; M.R. Apted &

S. Hannabuss, *Painters in Scotland 1301-1700 – a Biographical Dictionary*, Edina, Edinburgh, 1978; *Accounts of the Lords High Treasurer of Scotland, 1473-1580*, vols. i and ii, Edinburgh, 1877-1902; L. Bowditch, *The Thistle and the Rose*, Historic Scotland & National Archives of Scotland, official souvenir guide, 2002.

STEWART AND TUDOR COURT CULTURE: ARCHITECTURE

Richard Fawcett

This paper surveyed the development of royal palaces in the reign of James IV, a king who saw himself as much more of a player on the European stage than any of his predecessors and thus undertook building on an unprecedented scale: he formalised the emerging tradition of erecting principal buildings around a rectangular courtyard (with outer courtyards for ancillary needs).

Much less is known about the development of royal palaces before the late fifteenth century: nothing remains of the manor house at Cardross, Dumbartonshire, of Robert I (d. 1329); little survives of the L-shaped tower house of David II (d. 1371) at Edinburgh castle; Dundonald (Ayrshire) and Doune (Stirlingshire) castles were really fortified retreats, not palaces, but their plans illustrate the growing importance of the central courtyard to the early Stewart royals. Influenced by a long English captivity, however, James I (d. 1437) determined to give his kingship strong architectural expression. Although most of his palace works were subsumed by his successors' buildings he began projects at Stirling and built a large hall at Linlithgow along the east range which was perhaps intended to look onto a courtyard. James II (d. 1460) and James III (d. 1488) were both active builders although the former was more interested in artillery fortifications and little can be identified of the latter's projects. But much of their work would have been built over by James IV who transformed most of the royal residences.

At both Stirling and Edinburgh James IV erected private lodgings with large halls in the 1490s. But by 1500 at least he had moved on to build Great Halls for the attached castle residences: their grand scale necessitated hammer-beam roofs and, at Stirling (where the Hall is now refurbished), projecting window-bays at the raised stage (or dais) end with clear-storey windows. These works drew on some Scottish precedents but were also heavily influenced by English works. Contemporary influences from English architecture and English tradesmen working in Scotland can also be found at Linlithgow parish church and King's College Chapel at Aberdeen. All of these were projects in which James IV had a hand and were perhaps inspired by buildings like Westminster Hall (with its great hammer-beam roof) and Henry VII's apartments at Eltham (with its roof and dais clear-storey bay). However, perhaps because James himself had not seen these English works, his palaces retained a distinctly robust Scottish character of decoration and detail. Similarly, the corner angle towers of Linlithgow palace built in James IV's reign may also have been partly inspired by great English houses like Bolton and Lumley while the completed quadrangular ground-plan at Linlithgow echoes Henry VII's Richmond palace completed by 1501.

As a measure of the expression of power James IV wished to impart through his buildings, the forework at Stirling castle (completed *c.* 1510) provides a valuable case-study with a triple line of building works at the castle entrance constituting three-tier towers and archways, designed to give the impression of a castle from an Arthurian romance suitable for James' many tournaments. This may have been inspired partly by illustrations in manuscripts of which James commissioned several. But the king may also have been inspired by the multiple-tiered towers of French chateaux. The Scots had certainly taken architectural inspiration from French works in various religious buildings since the twelfth century. Moreover, James V (d. 1542) would make great stylistic borrowings from French sources which he actually visited for his works at Stirling and Falkland.

Overall, James IV was prepared to borrow architectural motifs to express his vision of kingship from both English and French sources but always allowed his native masons to complete works of unmistakably Scottish flavour.

Recommended further reading:– R. Fawcett, *The Architectural History of Scotland: Scottish Architecture from the Accession of the Stewarts to the Reformation, 1371-1560*, University of Edinburgh, 1994; R. Fawcett ed., *Stirling Castle: the Restoration of the Great Hall*, Historic Scotland 2001; J.G. Dunbar, *Scottish Royal Palaces*, Tuckwell Press, East Linton, 1999.

THE THISTLE AND THE ROSE EXHIBITION, STIRLING CASTLE, 20 MARCH TO 20 MAY 2002.

The exhibition contained the following key artifacts:-
The Book of Hours of James IV [Austrian National Library, Vienna].
Portrait of James IV with falcon (anonymous) [Stirling of Keir collection].
Portrait of James IV by Daniel Mytens [Stirling of Keir collection].
The Book of Hours of Margaret Tudor [Duke of Devonshire/Trustees of the Chatsworth Settlement]
Battle Standard carried at Flodden [Faculty of Advocates, Edinburgh].
National Archives of Scotland:-
> *The Treaty of Perpetual Peace.*
> *Papal Bull of confirmation.*
> *Treasurer's Accounts.*
> *Act of Parliament.*
> *Royal Letter Book.*

Ratification of the Marriage Contract [Public Record Office, London].
Portrait of Henry VII [Society of Antiquaries, London].
Bannatyne Manuscript [National Library of Scotland].
Hilt of a Sword from Flodden [National Museums of Scotland].
Portrait of Margaret Tudor by Daniel Mytens [The Royal Collection].

For more details see L. Bowditch, *The Thistle and the Rose* (Historic Scotland & National Archives of Scotland, official souvenir guide, 2002).

BOOK REVIEWS

Stirling Castle: the restoration of the Great Hall. Editor Richard Fawcett. Historic Scotland, and reseach Report 130 of the Council of British Archaeology. 2001. 100pp. ISBN 1 902771 21 4. £19.95.

Well illustrated, its eight chapters provide both a site history and a case study in historic buildings restoration. We have Michael Lynch on the Hall in the time of Mary and James VI, Doreen Grove on the militarisation of castle and hall, Ingval Maxwell on first stage restoration 1964-84, Peter Buchanan on the later stages, Gordon Ewart on the archaeology, and Duncan Peet on surveying and recording the evidence – a two page bibliography gives sources – primary published and unpublished, and secondary. The list of illustrations is long, and useful brief notes are given on the contributors. A massive restoration, while not without controversy – in principle and in detail, is here suitably recorded.

Stone Age Alpha. Edward Peterson. PCD Books (the author, PH3 1JD). 200pp.

A rock art enthusiast makes this well illustrated contribution to our prehistory and carved stones literature. Its ten chapters range over – floods and life after deglaciation, Megalithic tombs and boulders, the arrival of farming, monuments and seals – bronze and stone, early culture of Wessex, and the early Christian Church.

R B Cunninghame Graham. Fighter for Justice: an appreciation of his social and religious outlook. Ian M Fraser. 150pp. priv. print. Ferndale, Gargunnock. (and Smith Art Gallery and Museum). £8.99.

The clergyman author had access to rare documents including the special collection in Dartmouth College Hannover, USA, though now accessable in NLS Edinburgh. RBCG's social outlook is discussed under such headings as – his civilising mission, his social convictions, his homage to science,his suffering and championing of the poor – the 'Aristocrat of Democracy'. Going on to the religious outlook, headings touched on include – the creator, bible, status of women, patriotism and war – a 'Knight of the Spirit'.

RSCG being FNH's People of the Forth (14), this book should be very relevant to some of this journal's readers.

A Visit to Dunmore Pottery: a contemporary account with additional commentary. Graeme Cruikshank. Scottish Pottery Studies No. 4. The Stirling Smith. 2002.125pp. ISBN 0 9525 332 78. £9.60.

The 'contemporary account' is a rare booklet *A Visit to Dunmore Pottery,* written c1887, in the time of the great man of the pottery Peter Gardner (1836-1902). The reprinting of the booklet with further research and illustration is now a subtantial contribution to the history of this great pottery, and a timely 'In Memoriam' in this centenary year of Gardner's death, which the Smith Art Gallery and Museum has notably marked with both this publication and a special exhibition.

WRITERS AND ARTISTS OF LOCH LOMOND AND THE TROSSACHS

The Scenery of a Dream

Louis Stott

midst Nature's old felicities
Rocks, rivers, and smooth lakes more clear than glass
Untouched, unbreathed upon

The American film producer Arthur Freed made what is probably the best MGM musical, *Singin' in the Rain*, and what was possibly the worst, *Brigadoon*. In 1953 he travelled the length and breadth of Scotland to try and identify localities where this story about a fairy village, unchanged for a hundred years, might be set. Infamously he returned to Hollywood declaring "I went to Scotland but I could find nothing that looked like Scotland", and the film, which was received with incredulity here [in Scotland] was shot on a set built in a Hollywood studio.

There are important truths here. Scenery is what people perceive it to be, and it is writers and artists who establish it in our minds. In some instances they create it.

For the present Britain's pre-eminent National Park is the English Lake District. It's identity is – to a very marked degree – a product of its highly distinctive literary associations. Rock climbers will dispute this, and assert that, say, Haskett-Smith and George Abraham had much more influence in establishing the identity of a National Park which conserves both Napes Needle and Scafell Crag. Others will assert that it was the natives – John Peel, Will Ritson and John Wilson Robinson – who made Cumbria what it is. Fell walkers will continue to believe that it was W.H. Symonds and J.M.B. Baddely who put what became the Lake District National Park into our collective minds (and it is very likely that the likes of Hugh Dalton, Tom Stephenson and Barbara Castle, the young bloods who gave political impetus to the establishment of the first National Parks, might agree with them). These figures, and countless others, contributed a very great deal to establishing the identity of the English Lake District, but it was and is the District's literary giants who first gave it real substance – we are talking of Thomas Gray, the poet with 'a parrot-shaped neb' who 'discovered' the English Lake District (and, for that matter, Scotland), of Wordsworth, of his sister, Dorothy, of Coleridge, De Quincey and Southey. We are talking, also, about John Ruskin, Arthur Ransome and Beatrix Potter.

How does our first National Park compare with the Lake District in this respect? James Russell Lowell the American poet dubbed the Lake District "Wordsworthshire". It is an annoying misnomer, but there is something in it. Wordsworth dominates the Lake District in a way in which no other writer dominates other landscapes. However, Scott occupies a somewhat analogous position to Wordsworth in the Trossachs: *Rob Roy* and the *Lady of the Lake* are the *Daffodils* of this part of the world. It is interesting to note how many of the same literary figures are involved in both the Lake District and the Loch Lomond and the Trossachs National Parks. Minor characters (by whom I mean those with 'walk-on' parts), like Thomas Gray and William Hazlitt, Charles Dickens and William Combe, turn up in both places. Sir Walter Scott, and Christopher North (Paisley's Professor John Wilson) were deeply caught up in the literary growth of the English Lake District just as Wordsworth and Coleridge were involved here. Indeed there was much comparing of notes and borrowing from one another. My *Scenery of a Dream* hints, I hope, at both Wordsworth and Scott. Here is Wordsworth's *Highland Girl*:

> And these gray rocks, this household lawn,
> These trees—a veil just half withdrawn;
> This fall of water, that doth make
> A murmur near the silent lake;
> This little bay, a quiet road
> That holds in shelter thy abode;
> In truth together ye do seem
> Like something fashion'd in a dream

And, here, Scott describes the Trossachs:

> Highest of all,where white peaks glanced,
> Where glist'ning streamers waved and danced,
> The wanderer's eye could barely view
> The summer heaven's delicious blue;
> So wondrous wild, the whole might seem
> The scenery of a fairy dream.

We certainly cannot lay claim to Wordsworth in the way in which the Lake District can boast about him, although what are sometimes thought of as two of his best poems *The Solitary Reaper,* and his sonnet about Scott entitled *The Trossachs* are Scottish. Being Wordsworth he also bequeathed us one of his worst poems – *Rob Roy's Grave* – but bad poems take on a life of their own and are not necessarily to be deplored as literary associations! McGonagall (who visited these parts and wrote about them) 'invented' the silvery Tay.

Equally the Borders will not permit Loch Lomond and the Trossachs to lay exclusive claim to Sir Walter Scott in the way in which the Lake District possesses Wordsworth, although it can be argued that with the *Lady of the Lake* and *Rob Roy* and aspects of several of his other novels and poems this is Scott Country. His influence extends from Stirling to Roseneath and 'Ave Maria' and 'Hail to the Chief' give Scott an international resonance which arises out of this district.

Both Wordsworth and Scott were 'sassenachs', as was James Hogg who followed Scott into the District; literary residents in the Loch Lomond and the

Trossachs have included Tobias Smollett, Neil Munro, R.B. Cunninghame Graham, A.J. Cronin, and Iain Crichton-Smith. The distinguished cast of literary visitors has included as well – Thomas Gray, Boswell and Johnson, Robert Burns, Thomas Carlyle, Charles Dickens, George Eliot, Harriet Beecher Stowe and Robert Louis Stevenson. A host of other authors, from Blind Harry and Ben Jonson to Helen MacInnes and Iain Banks have connections with the district.

Places in the Loch Lomond and the Trossachs with particular literary associations include Inversnaid, a literary focal point linking Loch Lomond with the Trossachs. If we were given to plaques in these parts this is what a plaque at Inversnaid might say:

THE FALLS OF INVERSNAID

Walter Scott, two of whose novels, *Rob Roy* and *Waverley,* are partly set in the district, first visited Inversnaid in 1792. The falls are situated at the heart of the RR Country. William Wordsworth, his sister Dorothy, and Samuel Taylor Coleridge crossed and re-crossed the Ferry of Inversnaid during a tour of Scotland in 1803, which inspired Wordsworth to write the poem *To A Highland Girl*. The many subsequent literary visitors to this place have included the American Gothic novelist Nathaniel Hawthorne, the Danish writer of fairy tales, Hans Christian Andersen, the German novelist and poet Theodor Fontane and the French novelists Charles Nodier and Jules Verne, both of whom set novels partly on Loch Lomond. The burn inspired Gerald Manley Hopkins – sometimes regarded as the first 'modern' poet – to write a famous poem celebrating *Inversnaid*. It is one of the most significant 'nature' poems ever written, highly relevant today. John Barbour, the medieval poet, was the first to describe Robert the Bruce's crossing of Loch Lomond near here.

Other distinguished Scottish writers particularly associated with Inversnaid include James Hogg, the Ettrick Shepherd, the historian Thomas Carlyle, the poet and travel writer, Alexander Smith, John Stuart Blackie, and the Scottish Renaissance poet William Dixon Cocker.

The literary character of the Loch Lomond and the Trossachs, like that of the English Lake District, is complex, and not dependent on a single figure, but rather on successive generations of writers. Indeed in the variety of their literary associations both of these districts resemble cities.

It is perhaps unfortunate that the district's best, and best-remembered, poems were written by Englishmen, but the district resounds in Scott's poetry, and in memorable poems by half a dozen other Scottish poets. It is a comprehensible source of aggravation that Dorothy Wordsworth and others continually make unfavourable comparisons between Loch Lomond and Ullswater, but the Wordsworths contributed in a significant way to the discovery of Loch Lomond which ought to be acknowledged. It is also true that Loch Lomond's literary giant, Tobias Smollett, was an exile, but, so, too, was Edinburgh's Robert Louis Stevenson.

There may also be a perception that the literary connections of Loch Lomond and the Trossachs are derived, by and large, from transients. This is so, but it is also surprisingly true of Edinburgh, and of other literary focal points. Indeed many travellers came specifically to see the scenes described in *Humphry Clinker*, or in, say, Gilpin's *Observations*. Indeed both Smollett and Gilpin greatly influenced the growth of the travel trade.

Although there are earlier factual accounts of the district, for example both Camden and Defoe allude to Loch Lomond, it was not until considerably after the Jacobite Rebellion in the second half of the eighteenth century that journals of tours became relatively commonplace, and writers became concerned with the appreciation of what they saw. Their journals became 'literary', some having considerable literary merit. Smollett, and others, asserted that Scotland was less well known at that time than was Japan. Burt's *Letters* were thus perceived as curiosities describing a primitive country; twenty years later Pennant's *Journals* described the scenery and manners of a much better known place. Johnson praised Pennant: "he observes more things that anyone else does", and his works were influential. Samuel Rogers, the poet, describes how his father visited Scotland, while his mother kept a copy of Pennant to refer to when she heard from him.

In Sir Arthur Mitchell's masterly *List of Travels and Tours 1296-1900* [1902] there are 856 entries describing journals of visits made to Scotland, a very considerable number of which, unsurprisingly, touch on Loch Lomond. Of course, this makes many of them repetitive, and of little interest, but Pennant was respected by the great men of his time, and his journals were published more or less straight away.

Some journals were never published, others were limited editions known only to a select few, and yet others were not published until long afterwards. It is considered that, had it been published at the time, Richard Pococke's *Journal* of the tours he made between 1747 and 1760, which are strong on Loch Lomond, might have been as famous as Pennant's, while, if John Wilkes's *Journals* had not been burned (by an Irish poet!), they might have been as notorious as Johnson's *Tour*. A Scotsman, the bookseller John Knox, made sixteen tours in the Highlands between 1764 and 1775, and knew more about them than anyone. He intended to produce a major book, *The Picturesque Scenery of Scotland*, which Farington and others were to illustrate, but it was abandoned on his death in 1790.

However, significant as Pennant was, the decade in which both he and Johnson visited Scotland also saw the publication of the highly influential *Observations* of William Gilpin. It was he who had tourists looking at specific views through 'Claude' glasses, or, failing that, between their legs; he was the apostle of the 'Picturesque'.

The 1780s saw Robert Burns, who made his West Highland Tour in 1787, gallivanting on Lochlomondside, and the visit of Colonel Thomas Thornton, who came in 1786, and who was, perhaps, the first to perceive Scotland as the paradise which - regrettably in the opinion of some observers – it became for huntin', shootin' and fishin'. In 1789 Samuel Rogers followed his father to Scotland, but, interestingly, he assiduously followed Gilpin rather than Pennant.

The next decade saw the first visits to Loch Lomond of James Hogg and Walter Scott, the arrival of a significant woman writer, Sarah Murray, and of a distinguished foreigner, B. Faujas de Saint Fond, a French geologist whose *Travels* are often quoted. James McNayr's first real guide book was published in 1797. Thomas Wilkinson, whose book about the *Scottish Mountains* influenced both the Wordsworths and Scott, was in the Highlands in 1797, and, in the same year, John Stoddart, accompanied by Jean Claude Nattes (who later published *Scotia Depicta*) succeeded, perhaps, in fulfilling Knox's aims, in providing a generously illustrated descriptive work. An exceptionally talented local author, Alexander Campbell, born at the foot of Loch Lubnaig, produced *A Journey from Edinburgh through parts of North Britain* [1802], with drawings 'made on the spot' by the writer.

The first decade of the nineteenth century had the highly significant visit of Coleridge and the Wordsworths. Dorothy Wordsworth's *Journal*, regarded by many as the finest piece of literature not intended for publication ever written, was not published in full until 1874. Samuel Rogers, who was in Scotland again in 1803 and then in 1812, criticised Wordsworth for this. Joseph Mawman's *Excursion*[1805] reproduced a Turner drawing, since lost, of Ben Lomond. In 1810 the publication of *The Lady of the Lake* took place, succeeded by the 'Waverley Novels', and the trickle of tourists, Carlyle, Keats and Southey among them, became a flood.

At first, it was the Trossachs rather than Loch Lomond that the tourists came to see. Jamieson, in his edition of Burt's Letters, describes the frustration which a Highland guide to Ben Lomond from Lochlomondside felt because of Sir Walter Scott: "The devil confound his ladies and his lakes, say I!" However, eventually, the combination of Loch Lomond and the Trossachs was irresistible. It turned Inversnaid into the literary focal point which it has remained, and which we illustrate on the back cover of this journal.

The district benefitted, too, from the growth of travel on the Clyde, by 1820 *The Steamboat Travellers' Companion* had been published, its doggerel celebrating both the River Clyde and Loch Lomond. In 1821 Charles Nodier, the distinguished French man-of-letters, made his *Promenade from Dieppe to the Mountains of Scotland* and set two short novels in the district. Amadée Pichot followed his friend Nodier in pursuit of Scott and produced his own *Voyage* but also wrote the text for the spectacular engravings in Francis Alexandre Pernot's *Vues Pittoresques*. Scott was illustrated (by Turner, and by not quite everyone else), dramatised, set to music, and translated. The Highlands, by which people frequently meant Loch Lomond or the Trossachs, 'unknown' a century before, had become a highly familiar place.

Robert Cadell (1788-1849), Scott's publisher friend, arranged for Turner to illustrate Lockhart's edition of Scott's *Poetical Works* (1834), and he visited the Trossachs for this purpose in 1831. Turner's exquisite pencil drawings of the district are contained in his *Loch Ard Sketch Book*. Horatio McCulloch (1805-1867), the most evocative of Scottish mountain landscape painters, executed one masterpiece, so far as this district is concerned, in 'Loch Katrine'[1866], a stunning picture of Ellen's Isle and Ben Venue from the Silver Strand, a point of view chosen by countless others. Alexander Smith, the poet and author of *A Summer in Skye*, commented of McCulloch's picture "As a view of Highland scenery we have never seen its equal, and no man but McCulloch could have produced it."

Not long after Turner William Henry Fox Talbot (1800-1877), the British 'inventor of photography' visited Loch Katrine in October, 1844 to make Calotypes of scenery associated with Sir Walter Scott, and, in 1845, published *Sun Pictures in Scotland* which included six views of Loch Katrine, which were generally considered to be amongst his most interesting photographs.

George Washington Wilson (1823-93) of Aberdeen became Photographer Royal to Queen Victoria, and established many very well known photographic points of view. He exercised an influence comparable with that of Scott on the development of tourism in Scotland and views in the Trossachs are amongst his earliest subjects.

A sure sign of common currency was the spoof. By 1821 William Combe, debtor, drunk and satirist, had created *Dr Prosody*, successor to his more famous *Dr Syntax*, to mock too serious an approach to the tour of the Scottish Highlands. Thomas Cook's tours began. However, between 1831 and 1835 Nathaniel Parker Willis, the American poet, was commenting in *Pencillings By The Way* about 'unmitigated vulgarians' on the the 'route of the cockney tourists'. The sense of exploration and discovery of the eighteenth century was over, but 'literary' visitors still came – Charles Dickens in 1841, George Eliot in 1845, Hans Christian Andersen, with an invitation to visit Queen Victoria in his pocket in 1847, Harriet Beecher Stowe in 1853, Nathaniel Hawthorne in 1855-57, Theodore Fontane in 1858, and Jules Verne, who also set a novel in the Southern Highlands, in 1859. Two of the century's most unusual poets, Arthur Hugh Clough and Gerard Manley Hopkins, were both briefly in the district.

Books became more sophisticated. The literary visitors mentioned referred in letters to their experiences, but the 'Tour' tended to become the province of lesser writers. Alexander Smith's *Summer in Skye* was an exception, an affectionate personal essay, an effective guide, and a witty and beautifully expressed book. In 1854, John Smith, the Glasgow Bookseller, born in Strathblane, published Hugh MacDonald's *Rambles Round Glasgow* which has the same personal feel as *A Summer in Skye*. It became an indispensible literary companion to the countryside so accessible from the city.

There were minor literary residents in the district during the nineteenth century, for example, John Colquhoun, the sportsman, and Lydia Walford, the novelist, but it was not until the twentieth century that literary notables, not quite in the same class as Smollett perhaps, but significant literary personages in their own right, manifested themselves again. Of these, Cunninghame Graham, hero of the Scottish Renaissance, was another exile who did however live in the district for a long time, and enjoyed thirty-odd years of attachment to Loch Lomond and the Trossachs. Neil Munro chose Helensburgh as his last home. His book about the *Clyde* delights in the district. A generation later James Bridie anchored himself alongside the likes of David Bone in Helensburgh. Of the four, A.J. Cronin's work is most firmly rooted in Loch Lomond and the Trossachs, but he fairly rapidly detached himself from the place. He enjoyed the greatest literary success of the four of them, but probably deserved it least. He died, like Smollett, a lonely exile in a foreign land. These four make a formidable collection of literary figures, pleasingly representing various genres.

The district's connections with twentieth-century poets are equally impressive. A brace of highly distinguished poets taught in Helensburgh. Day-Lewis mentions the place in his autobiography, striking a favourable grace note which ought to be set alongside Dorothy Wordsworth's more often quoted and less-favourable remarks, while Auden was put in touch there with Marion Angus by Helen Cruikshank. He was already writing his deceptively easy-seeming verses. The poets of the Scottish Renaissance may be less important, and are certainly less well-kent, than these two, but the district has significant associations with several of them. Of their contemporaries, Kirk from Dumbarton was a doctor friend of Bridie, and Cairncross, one of MacDiarmid's mentors, was Minister at Bowling. W.D. Cocker, in particular, and Sydney Tremayne, both of whom were journalists, also have strong associations with Loch Lomond and the Trossachs. Distinguished poets of a later generation include Maurice Lindsay, Iain Crichton-Smith and Tom Buchan, each of whom captured a sense of it on the page in distinctive ways.

I have already mentioned one or two artists in connection with Scott. It is not surprising that the district interested Victorian landscape painters, but this is not the place for a catalogue of their pictures. Indeed Hugh Quigley, the Stirling born author of Batsford's *Highlands of Scotland*, pointed out that the beauty of the Trossachs became "conventional and rather wearisome" providing too many pictures of the sort which used to fill postcard albums and decorate chocolate boxes.

One Victorian landscape painter who escapes this charge is another John Knox (1778-1845) whose spectacular views of Ben Lomond are to be seen in Glasgow. Nor can this charge be levelled at the district's connection with Millais or with 'the Glasgow Boys'. John Ruskin (1819-1900) and his wife Effie, and John Everett Millais (1829-96), stayed in the village of Brig o' Turk in 1853. It was here that Millais fell in love with Effie. Millais' famous painting of Ruskin in Glenfinglas is regarded as a masterpiece, and his notable view of Laura's reception of the proposal in Trollope's *Fineas Finn* has a hint of Loch Venacher about it.

Perhaps it was the connection with Ruskin that led 'the Glasgow Boys' to Brig o'Turk in 1879-81, but it was also its character as a 'Highland clachan'. They were not, however, interested in painting 'scenery', but in painting rural life truthfully. In any case it is agreed that the summers they spent together in the Trossachs (and at Rosneath and Cockburnspath) were critical to their development as artists, not so much for what they produced as for the conversations about painting which they had.

James Guthrie (1859-1930) was a central figure. He went with Walton to Brig o' Turk in 1879 where Crawhall joined them. In 1881 he made drawings for his most famous picture 'A Funeral Service in the Highlands', a notable painting of a grim scene which he witnessed at Brig o' Turk, and which he finished using models in a studio in Helensburgh. Joseph Crawhall (1861-1913) was a brilliant animal painter with a great love of horses. This gave him a common interest with Robert Bontine Cunninghame Graham in nearby Gartmore, and Graham wrote an affectionate sketch of him. George Henry (1858-1943), joined Guthrie and Crawhall at Brig o' Turk in 1881, and painted 'The Cottage on the Hill' and a charming picture called 'Brig o' Turk' – to be seen in Glasgow – which he finished in 1882. Edward Arthur Walton (1860-1922) who is also associated with Helensburgh painted similar 'rural' subjects. His fine 1879 picture 'The Brig o' Turk' is in Dundee Art Gallery.

The Scottish Academician Joseph Denovan Adam (1842-1896), famous for painting highland cattle, taught other artists to paint these beasts at Craigmill, Stirling. (Sir) John Lavery (1856-1941), another leading figure among the 'Glasgow Boys' was a famous portrait painter, who painted a notable picture of Loch Katrine. Both he and Crawhall were friendly with Cunninghame Graham and, in 1895, Lavery went to Gartmore to paint two portraits of him. Mention must also be made of David Young Cameron (1865-1945) who lived for many years just outside the National Park at Kippen is sometimes thought of as a

Glasgow boy but was not really one of them. He was an outstanding landscape painter and a fine etcher.

Finally there are two particularly interesting sets of Loch Lomond pictures by the Scottish Colourist George Leslie Hunter (1879-1931). They capture, in the houseboats along the Leven, an aspect of the Loch which has now gone.

I submit that the National Park's literary and artistic associations are of the first rank, and that they will be highly significant in establishing its identity.

Further Reading

Louis Stott as author, and as publisher Creag Darach Publications of Aberfoyle, has a series of books *Ring of Words* about the literary topography of Scotland which include – *Loch Lomond* (1995); *The Trossachs* (1997); *Argyll* (1997); *Stirling and Clackmannan* (1993). Also *Enchantment of the Trossachs* (1992) on the fairy traditions of the area.

On the artists of the Trossachs a full treatment is given by Stott in his paper 'Art in the Trossachs' in the *Forth Naturalist and Historian* volume 24, 2001, pp 111-137.

BOOK REVIEWS

Alva 1900-2000: one hundred years of a Hillfoots town. Norman Dovey. Dovey. 2002. 50pp. £5.

A chronicle of Alva people and events continuing the story blazed for earlier times by the Libraries book *The History of Alva and District from the early Christian period to 1900.*

Bannockburn 1314: Robert Bruce's great victory. Pete Armstrong, illustrated by Graham Turner. Osprey Publishing. 2002. 96pp. ISBN 1 85532 609 4. £12.99.

Two *Bannockburn 1314*'s within two years!, Nusbacher's reviewed in *FNH* volume 24, is the larger, he was the historical consultant for the tv documentary. Armstrong and Turner have researched and published much, and with Osprey, on medieval modelling and illustration. Both are well produced, indexed and referenced, Armstrong's the more popular and striking in appeal. With the Forth Naturalist and Historian's particular interest in the Torwood we see it much noted by Nusbacher but not at all by Armstrong, an indicator of the Nusbacher's depth of treatment, as is his bibliography; similarly for the Templars and other subjects, but the Osprey book is the more attractive to browse, and to the pocket. It was well displayed at the NTS Bannockburn Centre's spectacular battle 'Reenactment' over the two days at end of August 2002.

In the Footsteps of William Wallace. Alex Young and Michael J Stead. Sutton Publishing. 2002 190pp. ISBN 0 7509 259 1 4. £25.

Young the writer and Stead the photographer take us on a well illustrated journey through scenes, places and monuments associated with Wallace, and while tracing his life as brigand, victorious and failed commander, and diplomat, they consider his relationships with key people of his time – Stewarts, Bruces, Comyns, Balliol, Edward. The complex of legends, authorities, controversies, sources, are recorded, well quoted from, and discussed. The Torwood and its Wallace Oak so featured by the Forth Naturalist and Historian are not here, indeed the Elliot Forest by Moffat and the ancient Ettrick Forest are featured as key campaign bases. The author poses that historians must recognise the importance of the development of traditions in their continuing investigations, which while short on knowledge of the hero have revealed much about the world of his time. This is a worthy read searching for the real life Wallace.

Francis Frith's Picturesque Harbours. Raymond Solby. Frith Book Co. 2001. 120pp. ISBN 1 85937 208 2. hbk £14.99.

Frith, pioneer Victorian era founder of the famed photographic archive, having made his fortune in his 30s by selling his Liverpool wholesale grocery, is inspired by photography to make wide ranging and exotic journeys, eg. to the Nile from 1856 – 60 years before the Stanley / Livingstone meeting. Largs, Oban, Tarbert, Rothesay, are among these maritime examples of his travels' stunning art.

THE STIRLING UNIONIST CLUB 1901 to 1919

David Perry

On Friday December 20th 1901 the following notice appeared in the *Stirling Journal & Advertiser*:

Unionist Club for Stirling

We beg to remind our readers that the Unionist Club in the Union Hall, Thistle Street will be opened at 8 o'clock. All Unionists will be welcome.

And so it was that the Stirling Unionist Club formally came into being. The *Stirling Journal & Advertiser* reported on this momentous event thus:

Opening of a Unionist Club in Stirling

Some time ago the leaders of the Conservative & Unionist Party in Stirling leased a portion of the old Union Hall in Thistle Street in order to fit it up as a political club which has been for long a felt want in Stirling. Tradesmen have been engaged on the premises during the past few weeks making the necessary alterations, & this work has now been completed as far as it is to be carried out at present. The result is a commodious and comfortable club where members can meet from time to time to read the magazines and papers, or spend an hour at billiards, chess or draughts. The opening ceremony took place on Friday night.

J.B. Richardson was in the Chair and the platform party consisted of: John Paton, Ex-Provost Yellowlees, John Monteath, D.W. Logie, Charles Wilson, A.G. Graham, T.W.R. Johnstone, M. Yorke, A.C. Buchanan, Henry Robb and Robert Whyte.

The Chairman welcomed the company to the first meeting of the club. It was by name a Constitutional or Unionist Club and all the members were expected to be loyal to King Edward VII and to the British Empire (Applause).

It was a social and educative club, not merely a club for amusements and pastimes, but a club to educate working men of this burgh in a proper way of thinking.

The Chairman had read a paper a few weeks ago "Organisation" at the Albert Hall on the need to improve their organisation. Now they had a club to meet in. Their main interest was to do everything in their power, leaving no stone unturned, until they had ousted Sir Henry Campbell-Bannerman from these burghs. They had thrown down the gauntlet and they could not look back. Every man of them must go forward and do his utmost for that purpose......

There was much more in this vein.

Thus the Stirling Unionist Club was set up to pursue the political aims of its founders. The club was there to provide social activities for its (gentlemen) members, but they were meant to support the political objectives:
- to ensure Ireland remained within the United Kingdom,
- to support the British Empire,
- and to oust the Liberals from power and replace them with Unionists.

HISTORICAL BACKGROUND AROUND THE TIME OF THE
FORMATION OF THE CLUB

Towards the end of the 19th century there were two political parties: the Conservatives and the Liberals. The Conservatives were led by Lord Salisbury and the Liberals by William Gladstone (died 1898).

Gladstone was very keen to solve the "Irish Question". The country of Ireland was then one unit, and wished to be independent of Great Britain. Gladstone supported Irish Independence and in 1886 unsuccessfully introduced his Home Rule for Ireland Bill. Ireland would have Home Rule, but would still pay taxes to Britain and send members to Westminster. Many politicians were against independence and wished Ireland to remain united with the rest of Britain, and hence they called themselves Unionists. Both the Liberal and Conservative parties had Unionist sympathisers and hence there were both Liberal Unionists and Conservative Unionists.

The Liberal Unionists were led by Joseph Chamberlain and their policies were much the same as the Conservatives. From 1886 to 1892 the Conservatives were in power, in alliance with the Conservative Unionists and Liberal Unionists. Gladstone's Liberals won the election of 1892 and made one last attempt to bring home rule to Ireland. Gladstone personally piloted the Bill through the Commons but he was defeated by the Lords. He then resigned and the new Prime Minister was Lord Rosebery. His government resigned in 1895 and the Conservatives, again supported by the Unionists, resumed power.

At the time the Stirling Unionist Club came into being (December 1901) the government was Conservative and Unionist, led by Lord Salisbury. However the member for the Stirling Burghs was the Liberal Leader of the Opposition, Sir Henry Campbell-Bannerman, who was not a Unionist. He strongly advocated Home Rule and was a considerable thorn in the flesh of the Stirling Unionists at the turn of the century.

Another major issue at this time was the war in South Africa. What we now know as the Union of South Africa comprised the four provinces of Cape of Good Hope and Natal controlled by the British, and Transvaal and the Orange Free State, controlled by the Boers (the descendants of the original Dutch settlers).

Joseph Chamberlain (a Liberal Unionist Alliance MP within the Conservative government) was the Colonial Secretary, and he, together with Cecil Rhodes, had expansionist ideals. They wished to annexe Transvaal and the Orange Free State but the Boers had other ideas. The war began in 1899. At first the Boers were successful and laid seige to British strongholds in Mafeking and Ladysmith. However the Boers were mainly farmers and were overwhelmed as British professional soldiers were poured in. The main war was virtually over by the end of 1900, but a guerilla war ensued until peace was finally made in May 1902.

Campbell-Bannerman's particular interest was South Africa and he accused the Conservatives of being warmongers. He was prepared to strike a deal with the Boer Generals and accused the British Government of excessive brutality in carrying out the war effort. The Unionists were incensed and responded that the Government had done everything they could to prevent the war starting, but now they were in it they were determined to bring the Boer Colonies into the British Empire. Consequently the Stirling Unionists were implacably against Campbell-Bannerman.

The enthusiasm and drive of local businessmen James Brown Richardson and Ex-Provost Robert Yellowlees led to the formation of the Unionist Club where members could meet in comfort and indulge in political debate. The presence of T.W.R. Johnstone on the committee was extremely significant. As editor of the *Stirling Journal*, publicity could be given to the activities of the club. Many a vitriolic article was published rubbishing the speeches of the Stirling Burghs MP Sir Henry Campbell-Bannerman.

A LETTER TO THE PRIME MINISTER

June 6th 1902 was a big day and the Committee resolved to send a letter of congratulation to the Prime Minister the Marquis of Salisbury and members of the government on the conclusion of the South African war. The letter was couched as follows:

The members of the Stirling Unionist Club unite in congratulating His Majesty's Government on peace being proclaimed in South Africa and on the eminently satisfactory terms of settlement by which it has been attained. They feel that the country has been laid under a deep debt of gratitude to them for the determined and yet most humane manner in which the prolonged struggle was maintained, for having steadily kept in view and completely secured the objects for which the war was waged, and for the admirable diplomatic skill by which an amicable pacification may now be regarded as assured. It was further resolved that a copy of this resolution be forwarded to the Most Honourable Marquis of Salisbury, Right Hon A Balfour, Right Hon Jas Chamberlain, Rt. Hon John Roderick and James McKillop MP.

THE PRIME MINISTER RETIRES

The committee liked to make their presence felt and on 20th July 1902 decided to send a letter of congratulation to the new Conservative Prime Minister Arthur Balfour following the retirement of Lord Salisbury (Robert Cecil). Sir Henry Campbell-Bannerman still of course represented Stirling Burghs.

The Stirling Unionist Club cordially offer you their sincere congratulations on your being called to be Prime Minister: and especially on the unanimity with which all parties have concurred and rejoiced in your promotion to the dignified office. Although on political questions we cannot agree with the present representative of the Stirling District of Burghs, we feel that when, in his place in Parliament, he addressed you in words of welcome and of appreciation he expresses the sentiments of all his constituents, and not least of those who are members of this club. With the assurance that by the blessing of Providence the affairs of the British Empire are safe under your guidance, and wishing you much personal satisfaction and great success in the discharge of your more onerous and yet most honourable duties:- I am, sir,

> *Yours respectfully*
> *J. B. Richardson*
> *President of the Stirling Unionist Club*

The committee further decided to send the following extract from the minutes to the Marquis of Salisbury:

The Stirling Unionist Club join in the universal regret that Lord Salisbury has now asked relief from the position of Prime Minister which he has occupied for seventeen years with the greatest dignity, wisdom and success. They trust that the noble Marquis may yet be spared many years to enjoy the retirement so nobly earned; and that as opportunity offers the Empire may yet continue to profit in home affairs and in foreign relations by his matured experience, his clear vision, his wise counsel and his high ideals.

Letters of acknowledgement and thanks were received from the recipients.

THE FIRST AGM

The first AGM of the club took place on October 10th 1902. The membership had reached 560.

The Vice-President, ex-Provost Yellowlees said that the club had attracted many members and was in good financial health. As an educative agency many lectures on political subjects had been given. Members have had an opportunity of being grounded in Unionist principles; the club also supplied recreation for the young men of Stirling, to have unrestrained intercourse with their friends and engage in healthy amusements free from insidious temptation (Applause).

On the 9th November, the club faced a major loss with the sudden and unexpected death of their President James Brown Richardson (aged 65). J.B. Richardson was the major force in starting the Stirling Unionist Club. He started his working life with George Younger and Co., Brewers of Alloa, as a traveller for 22 years. He left to go to James Harvey and Co., Distillers of Paisley, which he eventually took over. He had been a Unionist since the start of the movement 18 years earlier, and was actively involved in making speeches throughout the Stirling Burghs. He appreciated the need of effective organisation which included the formation of a formal club. His energy brought the club into being and his enthusiasm contributed mainly to its success.

The death of J.B. Richardson hit the club very hard, and no political meetings took place during the winter of 1902/1903. However, the social and recreational activities continued. Ex-Provost Yellowlees was elected as the next President.

On August 22nd the ex-Prime Minister Lord Salisbury died at his home Hatfield House. Sadly he had survived only thirteen months in retirement despite the best wishes of the Unionist Club. Born Robert Cecil in 1830, his family had been in the ruling classes since the reign of Queen Elizabeth I.

The second AGM was held on October 9th 1903 and decided to resume the practice of holding monthly meetings.

The first of these concerned the fiscal question. The Conservative and Unionist Government wished to impose tariffs on imports just as other countries did, giving preferential rates to British Empire countries where possible. Some Liberals, led by Sir Henry Campbell-Bannerman, opposed tariffs because they would increase prices and be unfair to those on fixed incomes. These Liberals were called Free Traders. Speakers were invited who supported the Unionist position. History reveals that the policy of imposing Tariffs was disastrous and led to a Conservative and Unionist wipe-out in 1906.

1904 was a quiet year, the monthly meetings being of a more sedate and recreational nature. At the AGM on October 14th the Chairman put the lack of political activity down to the unsettled condition of the Parties. He said that in the Stirling Burghs constituency they had in the person of Sir Henry Campbell-Bannerman someone of high position in the political world, and they needed to find a worthy opponent.

THE ELECTION OF 1906: CHARLES KENNETH MURCHISON

The Unionists knew that a General Election would have to take place towards the end of 1905. During the winter of 1904/05 a candidate was found in the person of Charles Kenneth Murchison. He lived in Hertfordshire, England. Aged 33, he was of Scottish descent, a partner in Basil Woodd & Son, Wine Importers. He was a member of Hertford Town Council and had been Mayor in 1902/03. He was a good speaker, a keen Unionist and prepared to stand against Sir Henry.

The Unionists swung into action. Murchison was introduced to the members of Stirling Unionist Club on 30th March 1905. A full account is given in the *Stirling Journal & Advertiser* of 31st March.

Over the next months, Kenneth Murchison addressed meetings throughout the constituency, which included Dunfermline, Inverkeithing and Culross. At the fourth AGM on the 10th October 1905 much was made of the opportunity to oust Sir Henry. The invited speaker, Mr C. Murray Stewart of Dunblane said that they had a good candidate who had courageously set out to attack the Radical's Goliath and it was a task that deserved every encouragement and unswerving support. (Unionists referred to Liberals as Radicals).

At the end of November 1905, Balfour and his Unionist Government resigned, and Sir Henry Campbell-Bannerman became Liberal Prime Minister. He was 70 years old and in poor health and his advisers wanted him to go to the House of Lords. But he wanted to be Leader of the House of Commons and his will prevailed.

Sir Henry called the now overdue election for Friday 19th January 1906. The moment the Unionists had been working for had come. Murchison was formally adopted as candidate for the Stirling Burghs on Saturday, 6th January. He was due to address his first meeting on Monday, and there followed a heavy schedule.

The day after his adoption, Murchison was struck by a severe bout of influenza. His temperature after two days reached 104.6°, and his doctor recommended that he should not get up that week. The election committee filled in for his meetings but realised that, as a relative stranger to the district, personal appearances by the candidate were essential. Therefore on 12th January the Unionists withdrew their candidate leaving Sir Henry to be elected unopposed.

What a bitter pill this must have been to swallow! Actually there was probably little difference whether or not the Unionist candidate stood. In this election the Liberals won a landslide victory. In the neighbouring constituency of Stirlingshire the Unionist sitting member, the Marquis of Graham, was beaten by the Liberal D. Smeaton. And in his home constituency, the Prime Minister was unlikely to lose.

As a post-script to Kenneth Murchison, his troubles were not over. On the day of the election he was declared out of danger. Two days later he was diagnosed as having scarlet fever, and was confined to the Combination Fever Hospital at Kildean for three weeks. He formally withdrew as a future candidate on 6th August 1906. But his luck changed and six months later he was elected onto London County Council.

THE CAMPBELL-BANNERMAN YEARS

On 30th November 1906 an editorial in the *Stirling Journal and Advertiser* (which was unashamedly Unionist) reflected the voting habits of the time. The Prime Minister wished to put through a Bill that one man should only have one vote. A man had a vote if he had property. If he owned property in more than one constituency he was entitled to vote in each. The Government wanted to exact severe penalties on those who voted more than once. The *Journal* stated the Unionist position: the Bill was a move by the Radicals to favour their party at the polls because they thought that Unionists were more likely to be multiple property owners and should be disenfranchised.

Then there was the problem of female suffrage. A widow may have considerable property and no vote. But supporters of female suffrage wished all married women to have the vote – to which there were grave objections. Ladies could only be prevented from gaining admission to Parliament with great difficulty. Few people could contemplate without dismay the prospect of a Parliament with both sexes.

Meanwhile women Unionists were becoming active, and a Women's Unionist Association was started in Stirling in 1906. The leading members seemed to be the wives and daughters of members of the Unionist Club. They of course could not meet in the Club, but held meetings in the YMCA Hall, Dumbarton Road.

The leader of the local suffragettes was Mrs T.W.R. Johnstone, the wife of the editor of the *Stirling Journal & Advertiser*. She invited Miss S. Pankhurst to address them at the lesser Albert Hall in November. The ladies were becoming more numerous and active than the men.

Throughout 1907 there was a noticeable falling off in attendance at the monthly Unionist Club political meetings and at club evenings. The excitement of the election was past, and members did not support the political meetings.

In an effort to regain the interest of members, a new prospective candidate was adopted in November 1907: Mr. William Whitelaw of Nairn. He was Chairman of the Highland Railway Company and thought that the fifty or so railway companies in existence were not efficient for the conduct of trade and the safe carrying of the public. Amazingly, he recommended nationalisation of the railways.

Simultaneous with this adoption, Sir Henry Campbell-Bannerman fell suddenly ill during an address at Bristol. All of Stirling Burghs, including the Unionists, expressed their regret. The Unionists thought that it was unlikely Sir Henry would remain in office, and there might be an election. Mr Whitelaw addressed meetings at Dunfermline, Inverkeithing, South Queensferry, Culross and Stirling. At one meeting a Radical was heard to remark "That's the best man the Tories have brocht forward yet." High praise and thought to be well deserved by the Unionists. His main platform was Tarriff Reform, the implementation of taxes on foreign goods so that they could be sold on an equal basis with home goods. He also wished to ride on the tide of Imperialism, emphasising that voters were members of a nation and an enormous empire.

Sir Henry Campbell-Bannerman remained Prime Minister until April 1908. In February, his health deteriorated due to heart problems. He hung on till April 3rd and then resigned. He died 19 days later. He was regarded as of average ability in opposition yet became a successful Prime Minister.

The Unionists joined with the general population in mourning the passing of Sir Henry but relished the prospect of a bye-election. Sir Henry had been the member for Stirling Burghs for forty years and the voters looked on him as their own. Now all this had changed and the voters were free to choose for themselves.

The Unionists thought that the Liberals might offer the seat to Winston Churchill. He had not won a seat at the General Election and had just been defeated at a bye-election at Northwest Manchester. However the Party officials decided against this move, and Arthur Ponsonby, Sir Henry's Private Secretary, was the chosen candidate. The Stirling paper noted "The Stirling Burghs were fortunate enough to escape from the embraces of Mr. Winston Churchill."

The Stirling Unionist club now prepared a punishing series of meetings for their candidate during a short sharp campaign of three weeks. On May 22nd 1908, Ponsonby was returned as Liberal member with a majority of 1361. In the national papers, Whitelaw was regarded as a good Scottish candidate who polled the greatest number of Unionist votes ever. However the Liberals had turned out in great numbers. The *Scotsman* noted "Stirling Burghs rejected a good Scotsman because he is a Unionist and returned an untried Englishman because he says he is a Liberal."

THE YEARS 1908-1914

On 14th December 1908, another stalwart and founder member Ex-Provost Yellowlees died, aged 66, after a bout of pneumonia following a chill. He had worked in his father's tannery business. In 1878 he was elected to the town council and became Provost in 1882, a post he held for nine years. Originally a Liberal, he had opposed Gladstone's Home Rule for Ireland Bill and from that time was a committed Unionist. The Unionist Club benefited from his business knowledge and his unswerving loyalty to the Unionist Party which made him a President who commanded respect.

In April 1909, Chancellor Lloyd George introduced a familiar budget to overcome a £15m deficit, which had built up to pay for naval increases and old-age pensions. There was increased duty on spirits, licences and tobacco and new duties on land and petrol. Income tax was increased to one shilling and twopence, and there would be supertax on incomes over £5000 per annum.

There was an unprecedented campaign which delayed passage of the Finance Bill. The House of Lords refused to pass the Bill, saying that it should be submitted to the judgement of the country. Prime Minister Asquith proposed a motion that the refusal of the Lords to pass the budget was a breach of the constitution. Parliament was dissolved on 8th January 1910.

A new prospective parliamentary candidate was found. Mr R.K. Cochran-Patrick was a graduate of Cambridge and Edinburgh Universities, and had been called to the Bar in 1890. He was very active and gave speeches at Dunfermline, Stirling, Inverkeithing, Culross, and Queensferry. At the general election in January 1910 the Liberals again won, but the parliamentary majority was now narrow. Cochran-Patrick lost by 2052 votes to the Liberal Ponsonby.

In the House of Commons the Liberals and Tories were now about equal in number. The new Labour party had been reduced from 53 to 41 seats. Nevertheless the Labour Party and the Irish Nationalists now had some power. The Irish used their muscle to reduce the power of the Lords by demanding three resolutions:
   a) the Lords could not reject a money Bill:
   b) a Bill passed three times by the Commons yet rejected three times by the Lords still becomes law; and
   c) Parliament should be limited to 5 years.

All this was adopted. Then King Edward died in May 1910. The politicians felt that it would be unseemly to squabble until the period of mourning had passed.

The delayed general election was called for 13th December 1910. However the Unionists were not active as Cochran-Patrick had now withdrawn from the political scene. Therefore Ponsonby was elected unopposed.

The overall result was as before with fewer people voting. The Liberals were still in Government with the minority parties holding the balance of power. The power of the Lords was reduced according to the formula above, eventually by invoking the Royal Prerogative, which over-rules the Lord's wishes.

The Home Rule for Ireland Bill was introduced in 1912. But Ulster, the north-east province of Ireland did not want to be forced into an all-Ireland community. The Ulstermen raised an army to oppose Home Rule in their province, and the Southern Irish raised the IRA to conquer Ulster. Conflict followed in 1914, and in March the four counties of Ulster were offered exclusion (increased to six in 1918).

War broke out in August 1914 which put an entirely different complexion on matters.

THE WAR YEARS

On Wednesday 5th August 1914 the military authorities took possession of the club premises for the purposes of billeting troops.

A political truce was observed in Stirling. At the AGM on 8th October 1915 the committee reported that the political side of the club had become completely submerged as a result of the devastating war raging throughout Europe. They had carried out the wishes of the Coalition Government and lent their help to the town of Stirling to any duty which they considered might bring the war to a speedy conclusion.

At the AGM of 18th October 1918, the members debated changing the constitution. The Club as a Unionist Club should be wound up, to be decided after legal opinion had been sought. The members unanimously agreed to this.

The headline in the local paper of November 14th 1918 was:

"Germany admits defeat. How the great news came to Stirling. And the reception it received"

Bells rang out, and most people took an impromptu holiday.

Bonar Law called for the continued support of the Coalition Government. "The thing we care for most is to make the conditions of life of the vast majority of the people of this country as good as it is possible to make them."

THE END OF UNIONISM

A Special General Meeting was held on Saturday 10th May 1919. All reference to political activity and Unionist principles were deleted from the Constitution which was approved. The club's name was changed from The

Stirling Unionist Club to the Stirling Union Club. There was still Unionist activity in the Stirlingshire constituencies. But as far as the Club was concerned, members had no further interest in politics. In future the club was purely social.

Just as well because the main reasons for the Unionists' existence disappeared over the coming years. They would have been bitterly disappointed when the Home Rule for Ireland bill was passed in 1920, giving independence to all but the Ulster counties. And gradually the Empire was broken up as countries gained their independence and joined the voluntary organisation – the Commonwealth.

The club still exists today, although in a completely different form:- as a bridge club in Colquhoun Street, Stirling. They celebrated their centenary of existence on 20th December 2001.

BOOK REVIEWS

Scotland's Millennium Canals: the survival and revival of the Forth & Clyde and Union Canals. Guthrie Hutton. 2002. Stenlake Publishing. 160pp. ISBN 1 84033 181 X. £25.
The author as a key writer on, and campaigner for, mid Scotland's canals, here authoritatively and readably takes us through their origins and developments from the early years 1768-1820s, on through to the Millennium Link. restoration and a new beginning 1994-2002. Well illustrated throughout with the tenth and final Link chapter in colour, it has a four page bibliography, and a helpful index.

Shipping of the River Forth. William F Hendrie. 2002. Tempus. 128pp. ISBN 0 7524 2117 4. £12.99.
Another notable handsomely illustrated work from Hendrie, author of the Discovery series books on the River Forth, and the Firth of Forth, reviewed in FNH volumes 19 and 21. Of particular interest is the Upper Forth area, and especially noticed the Edinburgh Castle paddler at Stirling harbour.

Old Alloa. Guthrie Hutton. Stenlake Publishing. 2002. 50pp. ISBN 1 84033 132 1. £7.50.
Handsome illustrations well annotated with history, and with further reading guidance.

Forth area readers might note at times interests in the journals *History Scotland* from Aberdeen University and the *Scotland Magazine*.

THE REVEREND DUNCAN MACFARLAN (1708-1791) OF DRYMEN

John Mitchell

Introduction

Amongst the Church of Scotland's most colourful characters of the past, the Reverend Duncan MacFarlan has become a rather forgotten figure, to some measure the consequence of being overshadowed by the accomplishments of his son of the same name and calling. After initially succeeding his father as parish minister for Drymen in 1792, Duncan MacFarlan D.D. the son went on to a long and distinguished career in both the church and academic life, holding such appointments as the living of St. Mungo's (now Glasgow Cathedral), Royal Chaplain in Scotland to four successive sovereigns, Moderator of the General Assembly on two occasions and Principal of the Old College of Glasgow which later became the University.

Childhood and Student Life

Born on 9 June 1708, Duncan MacFarlan snr. is believed to have been an elder son of Patrick MacFarlan (wife: Janet Stewart), the tenant of Pollochro on the east shore of upper Loch Lomond. Unlike his younger brothers and sisters, whose birth can be found entered in the parish register for Buchanan, Stirlingshire, the place and date of Duncan's baptism appear to have been lost. There is every likelihood, however, that this important ceremony took place at the family's ancestral roots in the Parish of Arrochar on the opposite (Dunbartonshire) side of the loch, where at the end of their lives his parents were taken for burial. Unfortunately, there are no surviving baptismal records for Arrochar prior to 1759.

Patrick MacFarlan's lands and farm steading at Pollochro formed the northern most part of Craigrostan, an estate which had emerged after the partition of the Earldom of Lennox. To the south of Pollochro lay Inversnaid, which during Duncan's early childhood was held by one Robert Campbell, better known today as the celebrated Rob Roy MacGregor. Rubbing shoulders with the MacGregors in his youth may well have sowed the seeds for Duncan MacFarlan's familiarity with pistol and sword in later years.

Written references to Duncan MacFarlan's life only begin to appear after he was admitted to the Old College of Glasgow to prepare for the church. On the satisfactory completion of his theological studies, he was licensed by the Presbytery of Dumbarton on 5 December 1732.

Guardian of Arrochar Estate

The now Reverend MacFarlan did not immediately seek a permanent post within the church, opting instead for the position of factor for Arrochar Estate on behalf of the often absent Walter MacFarlane, the 20th Chief of the Clan and noted antiquarian. Duncan MacFarlan's appointment coincided with the building of the first kirk at Arrochar, which has led several writers to refer to him as the minister for the parish. This was not the case, but in all probability he would have acted as 'stand-in' for the incumbent as the occasion arose.

Although the learned Walter MacFarlane had turned his back on his forebears' long martial tradition, he apparently had no scruples about his factor using a strong-arm response to those who sought to make-off with Arrochar Estate property. Tall of stature and powerfully built, Duncan MacFarlan was just the man. One account from the Dewar collection of West Highland folk tales tells us that before going in pursuit of cattle reivers or other robbers, MacFarlan would cast aside the black coat and breeches of his clerical profession and don highland dress before strapping on his weapons. Few of the armed back-up he gathered about him could keep up the pace once that he and his hunting dog settled into their running stride. As to the fate of those miscreants who put up a fight when he eventually caught up with them, for the most part history has drawn a discrete veil.

Minister of Drymen

After some ten years of employment outwith the church, on 2 November 1742 at a meeting of the Presbytery of Dumbarton, the Reverend Duncan MacFarlan was presented as a prospective minister to the Parish of Drymen. In the absence of any objections to the settlement, he was ordained on 12 May 1743. Right from the start MacFarlan made his presence felt with the Drymen establishment, becoming involved in a dispute with the Duke of Montrose and the other heritors over the neglected condition of the kirk, manse and schoolhouse. This was followed by further clashes over control of the teinds (tithes) of the parish and inadequacy of his stipend. By dogged determination, in all of these quarrels with the heritors the Reverend MacFarlan eventually had his way.

A confrontation of a different kind involved the Reverend MacFarlan with a group of MacGregors, who demanded that the small child who had been brought to him for baptism be given the clan name, despite the fact that use of the name MacGregor was proscribed by law. MacFarlan stood his ground and refused in no uncertain manner, the gathered relatives having to settle for the infant being baptised in the name of Graham. To his parishioners the Reverend MacFarlan was more than just their spiritual leader, but also the upholder of public order, using the staff he always carried to impose rough justice on anyone who unwisely caused a disturbance. The reputation he acquired as 'a terror to evil doers' spread well beyond the bounds of Drymen.

Duncan MacFarlan embarked on matrimony late in life, in June 1768 marrying Anne Allan, herself a daughter of the manse at Rhu, Dunbartonshire. The first of three children was born when he was in his sixty-first year. After almost half a century's dedicated service to his charge at Drymen, the Reverend MacFarlan died in post on 30 June 1791. A man of his time, this 'terror to evil doers' now rests in peace with his wife Anne in the parish kirkyard.

Acknowledgments

I am grateful to all those historians listed in the references below who have recorded various aspects of the Reverend Duncan MacFarlan's life and background. In addition, my thanks go to Arthur F. Jones (Senior Information Services Librarian at Dumbarton) for generously making available his genealogical research into the MacFarlans of Pollochro. Also to Carol A. Hemfrey (Drymen & District Local History Society) for her assistance in the preparation of this paper.

References

Anon. (1854). *Munimenta Alme Universitatis Glasguensis* Vol III. University of Glasgow.

Anon. (1886). 'Principal MacFarlan' in *Memoirs and Portraits of One Hundred Glasgow Men* Vol II, pp 189-190.

Fraser, W. (1869). 'The Barony of Arrochar' in *The Chiefs of Colquhoun and their country* Vol II, pp 68-101. Privately printed, Edinburgh.

Gillespie, R. (1880). Nimmo's *The History of Stirlingshire* (3rd ed). Thomas D. Morrison, Glasgow.

Hemfrey, C.A. (2000). 'Renowned Residents' in *A Millennium Account of Drymen & District* pp 125-147.

Hutcheson, A.McG. (1996). *Rob Roy MacGregor* Pt I. Clan Gregor Society, Alloa.

MacFarlane, J. (1922). *History of Clan MacFarlane*. Clan MacFarlane Society, Glasgow.

MacKechnie, J. (1964). *The Dewar Manuscripts* Vol I. William MacLellan, Glasgow.

Murray, D. (1927). *Memories of the Old College of Glasgow*. Jackson & Wylie, Glasgow.

Smith, J.G. (1896). 'The Ecclesiastical History of Drymen' in *Strathendrick and its inhabitants from early times* pp 73-97. James Maclehose, Glasgow.

Scott, H. (1920). *Fasti Ecclesiae Scoticanae* (2nd ed). Vol III. Oliver & Boyd, Edinburgh.

Whyte, D. (1988). *Walter MacFarlane: Clan Chief and Antiquary*. Aberdeen & North East Scotland Family History Society.

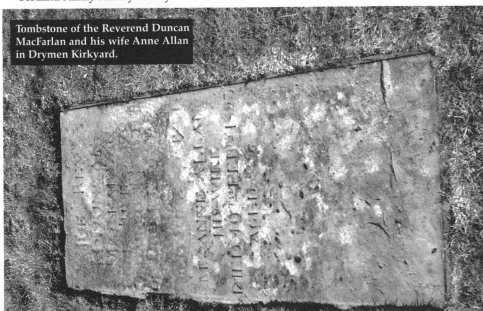

Tombstone of the Reverend Duncan MacFarlan and his wife Anne Allan in Drymen Kirkyard.

THE FORTH NATURALIST AND HISTORIAN

The Forth Naturalist and Historian (FNH) is an informal enterprise of Stirling University. It was set up in 1975 by several University and Central Regional Council staff to provide a focus for interests, activities and publications of environmental, heritage and historical studies for the Forth area, comprising now local authority areas Stirling, Falkirk and Clackmannanshire.

The promotion of an annual environment/heritage symposium called *Man and the Landscape* has been a main feature, and this year, the 28th, it's on Scotland's Weather & Climate – Living with Change.

The annual *Forth Naturalist and Historian* has since 1975 published numerous papers, many being authoritative and significant in their field, and includes annual reports of the weather, and of birds in the locality, plus book reviews and notes. These volumes (25 as of 2002) provide a valuable successor to that basic resource *The Transactions of the Stirling Field and Archaeological Society*, 1878-1939. Four year contents/indexes are available, and selected papers are published in pamphlet form, while others eg. Ashfield Factory Village, The Weather and Bird Reports, and Flora papers, can be available as reprints.

A major publication is the 230 page *Central Scotland – Land, Wildlife, People* 1994, a natural history and heritage survey, and used in schools throughout the area, also in the form of a CD-Rom, *Heart of Scotland's Environment* (HSE).

Other FNH and associated publications still in print include – *Mines and Minerals of the Ochils, Airthrey and Bridge of Allan, Woollen Mills of the Hillfoots, The Ochil Hills* – landscape, wildlife, heritage – an introduction with walks, *Alloa Tower and the Erskines of Mar*, and the *Lure of Loch Lomond* a journey round the shores and islands. Several of these are in association with Clackmannanshire Field Studies Society. Godfrey Maps have collaborated in producing old Ordnance Survey large scale maps of the 1890s for 24 places in the area.

FNH publications are listed on the internet by Book Data (thebookplace.com), British Library (BLPC) and by booksellers eg Amazon, Bol, Barnes and Noble....

Offers of papers/notes for publication, and of presentations for symposia are ever welcome.

Honorary Secretary Lindsay Corbett,
University of Stirling, FK9 4LA, and 30 Dunmar Drive, Alloa, FK10 2EH.
Tel: 01259 215091. Fax: 01786 494994.
E-mail: lindsay.corbett@stir.ac.uk
Web: http://www.stir.ac.uk/departments/naturalsciences/Forth_naturalist